THE COMPUTER

AND CHEMISTRY

THE

COMPUTER

AND

CHEMISTRY

An Introduction to Programming and Numerical Methods

T. R. DICKSON

Orange Coast College

W. H. FREEMAN AND COMPANY

San Francisco and London

To my family

PREFACE

The digital computer is one of the most important calculating tools available to chemists. Today its use is quite commonplace, and the chemists' ability to write and understand computer programs is becoming as necessary as the ability to use a slide rule. Many complex chemical problems, as well as those of a more routine nature, can be conveniently solved on a digital computer. Moreover, numerous industrial processes and an increasing number of research problems are greatly aided by computers. Many methods of calculation, methods that are complex or tedious when done by hand, can be accomplished with ease on a high-speed computer. Several computational techniques, such as Monte Carlo integration and iteration methods, are feasible when a computer is used to accomplish the calculations. In fact, many of the useful methods of numerical analysis can be employed by a chemist who knows computer programming and has the use of a digital computer.

The availability of digital computers is increasing greatly. The number of computing system installations in industry and on college campuses is growing at an enormous rate. Many schools have large computers available for use by various departments, and an increasing number of smaller computers are being installed for exclusive departmental use. Several schools have discovered that many industries have computing time that can be used for educational purposes. Because of the increase in the number of computers, more and more computing time is becoming available for use by undergraduates in many disciplines.

The purpose of this book is to provide a solid introduction to computer programming and numerical methods for undergraduate chemistry students. More specifically, the book is designed as a supplement to a second-year chemistry curriculum or a first-year honors course in chemistry. However, the book can provide basic background for any chemist or aspiring chemist interested in learning computer programming and numerical applications of computers. The text is written from a practical point of view, with the hope that the computer methods can be used to aid laboratory and theoretical calculations. The student is encouraged to write computer programs to solve problems ranging from basic stoichiometric calculations to numerical approximations of definite integrals. In this manner, the student can learn the programming and numerical techniques by applications to real problems.

The computer language in this book is FORTRAN, the one used most often by scientists and available for use with almost all makes of computers. FORTRAN is not, of course, the only computer programming language employed by scientists, but it is popular and general enough to be applied to many scientific problems. Furthermore, FORTRAN is a problem-oriented language; its computer programs can be used with most computers with little or no alteration. Since certain aspects of the language vary with the various makes of computers, minor alteration is necessary in some cases.

Several versions of FORTRAN are in use today; those appearing here are FORTRAN IV and FORTRAN II. Actually, all the computer programs presented are written in these versions of the FORTRAN language. Additional versions of FORTRAN, and several other computer languages, are best suited for share-time computer systems utilizing program input from a remote terminal. Systems of this type are not in wide use at the present time. Consequently, FORTRAN IV and FORTRAN II are probably the best languages to learn for practical purposes. In fact, knowledge of these versions provides a good foundation for the learning of other versions and other computer languages.

The first part of this book introduces the rules and procedures of the FORTRAN language. The examples and discussions are directed toward chemistry. This section is designed to provide the student with a working knowledge of the language so that he will be able to interpret FORTRAN programs and write his own programs. The second part presents basic numerical methods and the application of these methods to chemical problems that can be conveniently programmed. Actually, many of the methods presented can be used for calculation purposes even when a computer is not available. Also included in this section are numerous suggestions for programs that the student can write. In addition, many applications of the programs are given in the form of problems at the end of each chapter. However, the student is encouraged to apply his programs to specific calculation problems occurring in the laboratory or lecture. The intent of the second section of the book is to provide the student with the numerical methods that will permit valuable and meaningful applications of the digital computer. Finally, several appendices containing practical tips and necessary information needed for successful programming are included.

I would like to thank all those who have helped in the preparation of this book. In particular, I would like to thank Donald A. McQuarrie of North American Aviation Science Center for his review of the manuscript; my colleagues, James Wylie and Willard Roundy, for their critical review of the manuscript; Mrs. Nancy Riggs for her typing work; my students for their help and inspiration; and my wife, Margie, for her help and understanding.

May 1968

Thomas R. Dickson

CONTENTS

PART I

THE FORTRAN LANGUAGE

CHAPTER 1

INTRODUCTION TO

DIGITAL COMPUTERS

1-1. THE COMPONENTS OF DIGITAL COMPUTERS.

One of the excellent calculation tools available to scientists is the digital computer, an electronic machine designed to accomplish high-speed arithmetic calculations and whose basic components appear in Figure 1-1. As the figure shows, the central processing unit (CPU) directs and coordinates the functioning of the computer, controlling the other components and keeping track of the timing sequences involved in its operation. Included in the CPU is an arithmetic-logic unit that electronically accomplishes arithmetic operations and other logical functions. However, although the CPU is the basic controlling device in the computer, it could not begin to operate without proper instructions from a human operator. That is, the computer cannot function unless directed to do so by an operator.

One of the most important components of modern computers is the storage or memory core, which is capable of receiving information, retaining information, and making information available for processing. This storage consists of a three-dimensional array of toroidal-shaped ferrite elements called bits that can be electrically magnetized in one direction or another. Since these elements can exist only in one of two possible magnetized states, they are called bistable. These states correspond to the 1 and 0 conditions; that is, a bit is either in a 1 or a 0 state at a given time. The states of the bits can be read or changed electronically by the computer. By using the bistable nature of the bits, certain combinations of 1 and 0 bits can be utilized to represent a unit of information, which may be a numerical digit, an alphabetic letter, or some other special

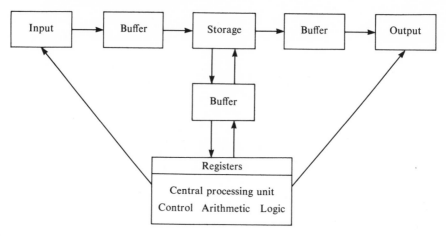

FIG. 1-1. Digital computer components.

symbol. In order to be able to represent many symbols, several bits must be used for each character of information. Consequently, each character in storage is in the form of a binary coded symbol that requires a group of 1 and/or 0 bits known as a byte. The number of bits in a byte depends on the design of the computer. Often it is necessary or desirable to have the computer work with a sequential series of bytes, called a word. Computers in which the words consist of a specified number of bytes are called fixed word length machines. Those computers in which the words are made up of a variable number of bytes are called variable word length machines. The word is treated by the computer as a unit of information, and can be considered the basic unit of storage. Each part of storage that can accommodate a word has a fixed reference number or address associated with it. Thus each word may be referred to by its storage or core address. The number of storage locations in a computer is often expressed in terms of 10^3 or K locations. A 20 K computer is considered a small computer, a machine with up to 100 K capacity is considered a medium-sized computer, and machines with capacities greater than 100 K are regarded as large computers.

When the computer is processing information, it requires a finite length of time to locate and transfer information to and from storage—this is called access time. Yet, in most computers, it is not practical to stop the CPU operation to wait for access time, and so, to prevent slowdown, intermediate storage units (called buffers) are used. Blocks of information are transferred from storage to the buffers, or vice versa, in order to conserve CPU operation time. Information must be readily available to the CPU during the period in which processing is being carried out.

Short-term storage units, called registers, are devices to which groups of words are transferred from storage so that the information contained in the words can be processed by the CPU. Besides allowing the information to be readily available while it is being operated on, these registers also serve as temporary storage of results before transmission to main storage.

Information is read into and out of the computer by use of input and output devices. In order to be placed in storage, information must be reduced to a symbolic form that can be interpreted electronically by the computer. This symbolic or coded representation of information must be placed on some input medium that can be used with some input device, and one of the most common of the input media is the punched card shown in Figure 1-2. Each punched card can contain up to 80 coded characters of information, which can be recorded on the cards by means of a keypunch. The keypunch is analogous to a typewriter, except that a character is recorded on the card as a specific combination of punched holes when that character key is pressed on the keyboard of the keypunch. The input device used with punched cards is the card reader, which detects the punched holes electrically and converts the information into a machine-compatible form so that it can be placed in storage.

Another common input medium used with many large high-speed computers is magnetic tape. (See Figure 1-3.) In this process, information to be used by the computer is recorded on magnetic tape and read into the computer by a tape-drive input device that converts the information to a machine-compatible form. However, the most common way in which the magnetic tape is recorded is by placing the information on punched cards and then using a computer to read the cards and record the information on magnetic tape for later use. The advantage of magnetic tape is that it enables information to be read into the computer quickly. Two other less frequently used input media are punched paper tape used with a paper tape reader and the electric typewriter, which can be manually operated and is connected electrically to the computer.

FIG. 1-2. Standard punched card showing character codes.

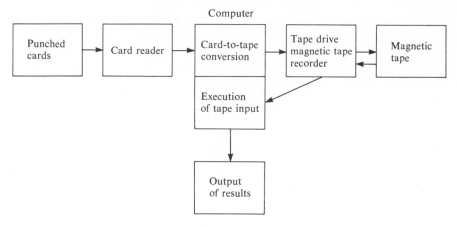

FIG. 1-3. Magnetic tape input.

Once calculations and data manipulations are carried out by the computer, it is desirable to have the results converted to a form that is conveniently understandable and that can be recorded on some output medium using some output device. One of the most commonly used output devices is the printer. A high-speed printer operated by the computer is used to output many lines of information per minute and to record the information on a printed sheet. A printer connected directly to the computer is called an on-line printer. A card-punch output device can be used to punch information on cards in a coded form, a convenient process and one that provides a good storage medium for information. High-speed output can be accomplished by recording information on magnetic tape via a tape recorder controlled by the computer. To convert punched cards or magnetic tape into a printed form, it is necessary to use a printer in combination with appropriate conversion devices. A printer that is not directly connected to the computer and that is used to convert tape and punched cards to a printed form is called an off-line printer.

1-2. COMPUTER LANGUAGES AND PROGRAMMING.

Each computer is designed to perform certain types of operations, and can be directed to do so by an instruction (command or order). The instructions, which can be given to the computer in a coded form by a human operator, define the basic operation and identify the data, device, or mechanism for carrying out the operation. A series or sequence of instructions designed to accomplish a specific goal is called a routine. For example, a routine may be a series of instructions designed to calculate the square root of a number. An entire series of instructions, including one or more routines, needed to establish the method of solution for a problem is called a computer program or simply a program. The individual who writes programs is called a programmer or coder, while the process of writing programs is called programming or coding.

A computer cannot execute instructions, or a program, unless they are contained in storage. Consequently, modern computers are called stored program computers. Once a program has been recorded on an input medium, it must be read into storage via some input device and only then can the program be executed by the computer. However, because this process is completely controlled by the human operator, the computer cannot function unless it is directed to do so by the operator. Furthermore, each step in the solution of the programmed problem must be precisely defined as an instruction. In other words, the computer cannot create instructions; it can only execute instructions that are read into it.

A program must be written in a coded form that can be interpreted by the computer. The choice of coded symbols is arbitrary and depends on the design of the computer. A system of symbols used to instruct or communicate with the computer is called a computer language. Generally there are three types of computer languages: machine languages, symbolic languages, and problem-oriented languages. Machine languages are basic, specific, used only on a computer of a given design, and are directly interpreted by the control section of the computer. Machine languages consist of digital codes representing specific instructions. However, the machine language of a given computer is the fundamental language, and all programs must be ultimately reduced to machine language form. Fortunately, most computers have a previously written machine language program, called a processor, that will translate and organize programs written in other languages into executable machine code, and thus knowledge of the machine language of a particular computer is not necessary.

The second type of computer languages, the symbolic languages, are those in which convenient mnemonic symbols are used in place of the digit codes of the machine language. For example, if the digits 21 indicate add in the machine language, then the symbolic representation may be the letter A. Although also designed specifically for a particular computer model, these languages greatly simplify the writing of complex programs. Once a program is written in a symbolic language on some input medium, it is converted by the computer into a machine language form by means of a processor called an assembler. This translation and conversion operation is known as the assembly process.

The problem-oriented languages are, in general, computer independent and designed for program writing without intimate knowledge of the computer. Often, with little or no alteration, a program written in one of these languages can be utilized on a variety of different computer models. In addition, they are specifically designed to allow for the convenient statement and solution of numerical problems. A program written in a problem-oriented language is converted to a machine language form by a processor called a compiler. The conversion process is known as compilation. The compiler is a more complex processor than the assembler because it is used to convert more complicated problem-oriented language statements into a series of machine language instructions. The most common of the problem-oriented languages are FORTRAN, ALGOL, COBOL, and PL/1. FORTRAN is the most widely used today. The FORTRAN and ALGOL languages, with their algebralike symbols, are used for solving mathematical and scientific problems, while COBOL (Common Business-Oriented Language) generally has business application. PL/1 (Program language, version 1), a new programming language that will soon be employed extensively, is modular in design and includes many of the features of FORTRAN, ALGOL, and COBOL.

Programs written in symbolic or problem-oriented languages are referred to as source programs. Computer conversion of the source programs into

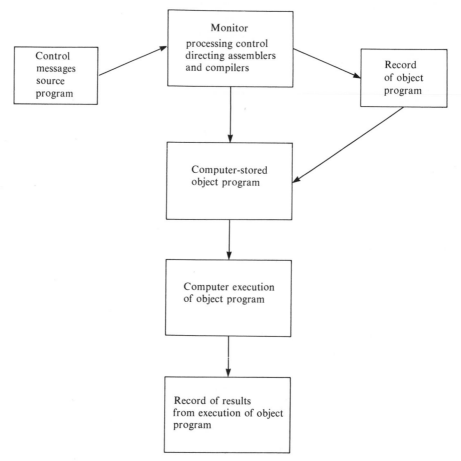

Fig. 1-4. Processing of a source program under monitor control.

machine language equivalents is accomplished by the processor. The processor is a machine language program designed to translate source programs. The translated form of the source program is called an object program. When using a source program, keep in mind that you are not actually directing the computer but are activating a processor—already in the computer—which prepares an object program that the computer can execute to achieve the results you desire. In most computer systems in use today, the compiler and assembler are included as parts of a larger supervisory program, a monitor; that is, a master control program that provides for the most efficient use of the computer with the minimum intervention from the human operator. A valuable function of the monitor is that it permits the processing of a series of source programs which can be assembled, compiled, and executed sequentially with no loss of time between programs. Referred to as batch processing, this system allows a large number of source programs to be processed in the minimum time interval. The monitor is controlled by monitor control instructions that precede a given source program and indicate to the monitor the specific operations to be carried out. Figure 1-4 shows a schematic representation of the processing of a source program under monitor supervision. The monitor control message indicates to the monitor the nature of the source program to be processed and also whether execution and/or recording of the object program is required. If some unforeseen error made the compilation process impossible, a message indicating error would be recorded by the processor, control would be transferred back to the monitor, and the next monitor message and source program in sequence would be processed. In other words, if an error arises, the processing job is terminated and the next processing job in sequence is begun. Good programmers save valuable time by double checking their programs for errors. However, if an error occurs, the program must be debugged; that is, the error must be isolated and corrected before the processing job can be repeated.

1-3. FLOW CHARTING.

In order to write an effective program for most problems, it is necessary to divide the problem into a series of simple, interrelated steps. This requirement ensures logical and effective coding. The best approach for devising a program for a complex problem is to indicate each step in a schematic representation of the logical solution of the problem. Such a representation is called a flow chart; and the process of devising a flow chart, the first step in the development of a computer program, is called flow charting. The flow chart provides for the organization and isolation of portions of the program that can be developed and then interconnected to other portions to give a logical picture of the overall program.

A set of special symbols is used in flow charting to represent various processes, and most flow charts can be devised with the basic symbols shown in

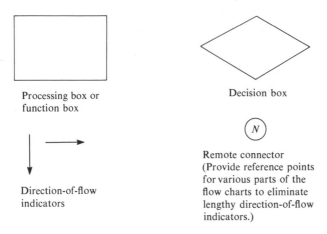

Processing box or
function box

Decision box

Direction-of-flow
indicators

Remote connector
(Provide reference points
for various parts of the
flow charts to eliminate
lengthy direction-of-flow
indicators.)

FIG. 1-5. Basic flow charting symbols.

Figure 1-5. The simple flow chart shown in Figure 1-6 describes the procedure used to determine the mass of an object on an automatic balance. Notice the step-by-step logical progress indicated by the flow chart and the points at which decisions are required. These points of decision permit the repetition of a given step, or series of steps, until the proper condition is met. This repetition process is called looping, and the series of steps involved is called a loop. Notice also that the remote connectors provide easy reference to various parts of the program and eliminate an excess of lines. A flow chart can be developed from the statement of a problem and can be quite general or quite detailed. Flow charting of complex problems is usually accomplished by making a general flow chart of the overall problem and then making detailed flow charts for the steps included in the general flow chart. As another example of the flow charting method, consider the following problem. It is necessary to solve a series of quadratic equations of the form $ax^2 + bx + c = 0$ using the relationship

$$x = \frac{-b \pm \sqrt{b^2 - 4ac}}{2a}.$$

The values of a, b, and c are to be read into the computer and the roots calculated and recorded for each case. When the quantity $b^2 - 4ac$ is negative, the square root cannot be obtained and the roots are complex conjugates. In this case, a message to that effect should be recorded. The program should be designed to accomplish the calculations for one hundred sets of a, b, and c values. A flow chart for a program to solve this problem appears in Figure 1-7. In the first step, K, the counter, is defined (initialized) as being equal to zero. A set of values of a, b, and c are input in the second step. The value of the discriminant, $b^2 - 4ac$, is determined, and then a decision is made concerning the sign of the

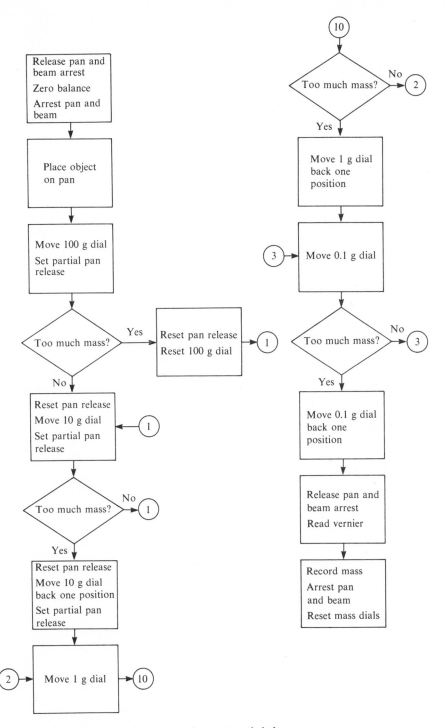

FIG. 1-6. Flow chart for the use of an automatic balance.

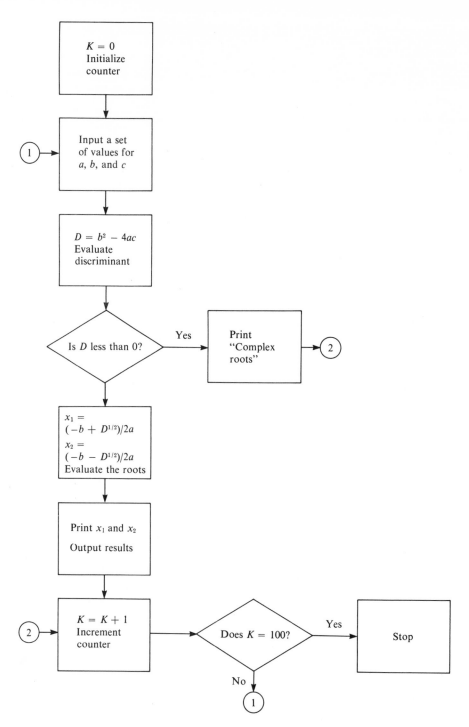

FIG. 1-7. Flow chart for the determination of the roots of one hundred quadratic equations.

resulting value. If the value is positive, the two roots are calculated and output. Next, the counter is incremented by one, and a decision as to whether or not the counter value equals 100 is made. If the counter equals 100, the process stops and, if not, the program branches back to the input process and repeats. In the first decision, if the discriminant had been negative, an appropriate message would be recorded and a branch to the tally point would occur. Once a flow chart has been developed, a program can be written with instructions corresponding to the steps in the chart.

CHAPTER 2

THE FORTRAN

LANGUAGE

2-1. BASICS OF THE FORTRAN LANGUAGE.

A computer language designed to solve problems in science and mathematics, FORTRAN (a contraction of formula translation) has various versions (levels), and, in a sense, each simpler version can be considered a subset of the next higher version. That this is not strictly true is due to the different varieties of computers. Moreover, differences exist in the rules governing the use of a given FORTRAN version when used with different types of computers. The versions discussed in this book are FORTRAN IV and FORTRAN II; it is important to note the differences between them as you read.

The fundamental instruction or sentence in FORTRAN is called a FORTRAN statement or simply a statement. A FORTRAN program consists of a series of statements, each serving a specific function. The statement may specify a calculation, logical decision, data manipulation, or some other function. Only a certain set of symbols may be used to form statements according to established rules. In fact, the FORTRAN language can be considered a set of rules (syntax rules) defining the proper arrangement of the language symbols that will provide for the proper expression of a problem. Consequently, to learn FORTRAN we must learn a set of logical rules that apply to the use of the language symbols. The symbols that may be used in FORTRAN are

1. The 26 capital alphabet letters; A through Z.
2. The 10 decimal digits; 0 through 9.
3. The special characters $+ - / * . = ,)($ \$ (blank space: represented as a lower case b for sake of discussion).

FORTRAN statements consist of specific combinations of these symbols, depending on the purpose of the statement. Statements can be classified according to their function.

1. Arithmetic statements, which specify mathematical operations.

2. Input and output statements, which call for the reading of data into the computer from an input device or for the output of calculated results or other information via an output device.

3. Specification statements, which specify the number and algebraic forms of the input or output data.

4. Control statements, which allow for the conditional or unconditional deviation from the sequential execution of the statements.

2-2. EXPRESSION OF CONSTANTS AND VARIABLES.

Before turning to the rules for writing FORTRAN statements, we should consider the manner in which numbers and algebraic quantities can be formed from the set of allowable FORTRAN symbols. FORTRAN provides for the definition, the expression, and the algebraic manipulation of constant quantities and variable quantities. Constant quantities are quantities having fixed and invariant values at given conditions. Several types of constants may be used in FORTRAN. One type is the integer or fixed-point constant, which may only have an integer value. An integer constant is formed by writing a sequence of any of the decimal digits without a decimal point. The constant may or may not be preceded by a plus or minus sign. If a sign is absent, a positive value is assumed. The allowable length of an integer constant depends on the level of FORTRAN and on the type of computer being used. This type of constant is sometimes called "fixed point," for an implied decimal point is considered to be located to the right of the low-order digit; this decimal point is never written.

1
+2
2
−1
17
+29
1296
0
−2222

The integer constant would only be used in a program where integer values are needed. For example, if a quantity was to be incremented by an integer in a program, an integer constant could be used; or, if we wanted to express a variable in subscript form, an integer could be used as the subscript. Since integer constants are expressed without any digits to the right of the implied decimal point, and there is a limit to the size of the constant, care must be exercised when arithmetically manipulating these constants. That is, if the maximum size of an integer constant is four digits, then the product, sum, or difference of two integer constants cannot exceed four digits. Furthermore, the division of one integer constant by another will only produce an integer quotient, and no decimal places to the right of the implied decimal point will be retained. Some examples of integer arithmetic appear below.

$$10 + 1 = 11$$
$$2345 - 5 = 2340$$
$$(20)(32) = 640$$
$$15/3 = 5$$

$(200)(125) = \underline{2}5000$ If the maximum size of an integer constant is four digits, the underlined 2 is not included as part of the computer-stored answer. The stored answer is 5000.

                        In the computer-stored answer, only the integer portion of the quotient is retained; so the underlined portion is not

$10/3 = 3.\underline{333}$ part of the answer. The stored answer is 3.

The maximum allowable number of digits and the maximum value that can be used in forming integer constants depend on the type of computer being used. Table 2-1 shows the standard length of integer constants for some computers.

TABLE 2-1. Standard Lengths of Integer Constants

Type of Computer	Maximum Number of Digits	Maximum Allowable Value $(+ \text{ or } -)$
IBM 1620	4	$10^4 - 1$ (9999)
IBM 360, RCA SPECTRA 70	5	$2^{15} - 1$
IBM 7040, 7044, 7090, 7094	11	$2^{35} - 1$
UNIVAC III	6	$10^6 - 1$
IBM 1400 series	20	$10^{20} - 1$

Note: In some cases, the standard lengths of integer constants can be changed by the programmer.

The second type of constant, the real or floating-point constant, is an invariant numerical quantity having a decimal point as part of the number. When a decimal point is present, the number is stored in the computer in a manner that differs from the storage of integer constants. Real constants can be formed in two ways—with and without exponents. Real constants without exponents are formed by writing a sequence of decimal digits with a decimal point in the desired position. This type of constant may or may not be preceded by a sign.

$$-273.$$
$$+22.4$$
$$0.0821$$

760.
5280.00
9.80665
−3.1416

All real numbers used in calculations and most easily written in a nonexponential form are expressed as constants of this type. Such constants are most often used as the numerical constants in calculations. The maximum number of digits that may be utilized to form real constants depends on the type of computer being used. Table 2-2 gives the standard maximum number of digits for some types of computers.

TABLE 2-2. Standard Lengths of Real Numbers Without Exponents

Type of Computer	Maximum Number of Digits (mantissa)
IBM 1620	8
IBM 360, RCA SPECTRA 70	7
IBM 7040, 7044, 7090, 7094	9
IBM 1400 series	18
UNIVAC III	10

Note: The standard length of real constants without exponents can be changed in some cases by the programmer.

Real constants with exponents are formed in a manner analogous to writing numbers in scientific notation. This form of a real constant is written as a signed or unsigned sequence of decimal digits, with a decimal point in the desired position, followed by the letter E and a signed or unsigned one- or two-digit number. The first part of the number is called the mantissa and represents the number that is to be multiplied by ten raised to the power given by the digits following the E. These constants are generally of the form $\pm.nnnnnnnnE\pm nn$. The decimal point may be located in any position desired. This form is a symbolic representation of the scientific notation form of a number and thus has the meaning $(\pm.nnnnnnnn) \times 10^{\pm nn}$. The allowable length of this type of constant also depends on the type of computer being used. Some examples of real constants with exponents are shown below.

Constant	Equivalent Scientific Notation Form
6.02E23	6.02×10^{23}
+2.997925E+8	$+2.997925 \times 10^{+8}$
16.0E−20	16.0×10^{-20}
12345678.E89	$12345678. \times 10^{89}$
−.022E−2	$-.022 \times 10^{-2}$
1.0E08	1.0×10^{8}
−.00000006E5	$-.00000006 \times 10^{5}$

This form of the real constant shows how the scientific form of numbers can be represented. Real numbers are written like this when it is not possible or convenient to write them in the nonexponential form. The standard maximum allowable size and magnitude of real constants with exponents for several types of computers are given in Table 2-3. Literal constants (alphabetic symbols) can also be defined, but these will be discussed later.

TABLE 2-3. Allowable Lengths and Exponent Range for Real Numbers with Exponents

Type of Computer	Maximum Size of Portion of Number Preceding the E (mantissa length)	Maximum Exponential Range
IBM 1620	8	10^{-99} to 10^{99}
IBM 360, RCA SPECTRA 70	7	10^{-75} to 10^{75}
IBM 7040, 7044, 7090, 7094	9	10^{-38} to 10^{38}
IBM 1400 series	18	See computer manual.
UNIVAC III	10	10^{-51} to 10^{49}

Note: The mantissa lengths can be varied by the programmer in some cases.

Occasionally a computer calculation requires more significant digits than are available in the normal real constant. Many compilers allow the programmer to specify the length of real and integer constants for a given program. However, since it is usually desirable to have more digits in only some of the constants, it is not necessary to have all the constants larger than usual. Most FORTRAN IV compilers provide for the establishment of specific real constants of from one to sixteen digits. That is, the compilers allow some constants to have a mantissa length up to sixteen digits. In fact, several are designed to allow even larger mantissa lengths. These longer constants, called double precision constants, are written as a signed or unsigned sequence of decimal digits, with a decimal point in the desired position, followed by the letter D and a signed or unsigned one- or two-digit characteristic. In other words, the form is similar to that of real constants with exponents except that more digits are allowed in the mantissa. The double precision constants have the general form:

$$\pm.nnnnnnnnnnnnnnnnnD\pm nn$$

where the decimal point may be in any desired position. The general meaning of such constants is

$$(\pm.nnnnnnnnnnnnnnnn) \times 10^{\pm nn}$$

Double precision constants without exponents are also permitted and are formed as a signed or unsigned sequence of from nine to sixteen (or more) decimal digits, with a decimal point in the desired position. In fact, any real constant used in FORTRAN IV with nine or more digits and no exponent is assumed to be a double precision constant. Some examples of double precision constants are

    −.1234567812345678D−22
    1.2345678910
    5.234567835D+2
    +3.141592653589793

A complex number can be expressed in the following general form:

    ±(real)±(imaginary)*i*.

Such numbers consist of a real part and an imaginary part. Several **FORTRAN** IV compilers provide for the establishment of complex constants to be used in calculations involving complex numbers. Complex constants are formed as a pair of signed or unsigned real constants separated by a comma and enclosed within a set of parentheses.

Complex Number	FORTRAN Notation for Complex Number
$+2.3 - 1.7i$	$(+2.3, -1.7)$
$6.7456743 + 0.0i$	$(6.7456743, 0.0)$
$1.72 \times 10^2 - 1.03 \times 10^1 i$	$(1.72E2, -1.03E1)$

FORTRAN IV compilers are able to respond to logical relationships between data in addition to allowing arithmetic manipulations of data. The nature and use of the logical relationships are discussed in Sections 2-7 and 3-2. In order to use such relationships, it is necessary to be able to establish logical constants. Logical constants can be expressed in two forms only:

    .TRUE.
    .FALSE.

These constants must be preceded and followed by periods for definition purposes.

Variables are quantities that may take on various values, depending on the conditions at a given time. FORTRAN variables, which are analogous to algebraic variables, are formed by certain combinations of symbols. Generally there are two types, integer and real (floating-point) variables. Integer variables are variables having only integer values. Names or symbols representing this type of variable are formed as a sequence of from one to six alphabetic letters or decimal digits. However, the names must begin with one of the letters I, J, K, L, M, or N. These six letters, when used as the first letter in a variable name, are reserved for naming integer variables. Any other symbols (alphabetic or decimal digit), except the special characters, may be used in forming the name of a variable. Some examples of integer variable names are as follows:

I	L	MN	IJKLMN
NCON	NCON1	NCON2	NCON3
INT	LVALUE	JTWNTY	NR
KONST	KOUNT	MOLVOL	NUMBER
I1	I12	I123	I1234

Whenever possible, it is often useful to give integer variables names that convey some meaning so that the nature of the variable can be kept in mind when it is used in the program. Notice that decimal digits are used as part of the names in some of the examples above. When used as part of a variable name, digits have no numerical significance and are merely symbols that the programmer may or may not choose to use when forming variable names. Variable names are limited to a maximum of six characters on most computers. However, the maximum allowable number of characters on certain computers may be greater or less than six. With some compilers, one possible limitation on the sequences of symbols is that if the name is more than four characters long it cannot end in the letter F.

Real or floating variables represent quantities that can assume real values. Symbols or names for this type of variable are formed as a sequence of from one to six alphabetic letters or decimal digits. The variable name must begin with an alphabetic letter. However, the name cannot start with one of the letters I through N, nor can it contain a special character.

FMOLES	GRAMS	PERCNT	PI
RESULT	SUM	SUMX	SUMY
FMEAN	SQROOT	CUBE	THIS
X	Y	A	B
XL	X1	X23	X1X1
ANS1	ANS2	ANS3	VOLUME

Note that useful names may be given to this type of variable so that the significance of the variable can be kept in mind when it is used in the program.

In FORTRAN IV, it is possible to use double precision and complex variables. Double precision variables, of course, are variables that can take on only double precision values, while complex variables are variables that can take on only complex number values. These two types of variables are named the same way that ordinary real variables are named. Whether a given variable is to be a standard real variable, a double precision variable, or a complex variable depends on the context in which it is used.

To avoid ambiguity concerning the nature of a variable, most FORTRAN IV compilers provide the programmer with the capability of specifying the nature of a given variable within a program. This specification is accomplished by a TYPE declaration statement. (The way in which statements are expressed and coded is discussed in Section 2-3.) The TYPE declaration statement permits the description of a variable or a group of variables as double precision, complex, logical, real, or integer. The declaration statement defines the variable type for a particular variable name and indicates to the compiler that the proper amount of storage must be reserved for the variable. Furthermore, the TYPE declaration statement can be used to override the rule concerning the naming of integer variables. The general form of the TYPE declaration statement is

kw $v_1, v_2, \ldots, v_n$

where kw is a keyword indicating the nature of the variables and $v_1, v_2, \ldots, v_n$ is a list of one or more variable names of the type specified by the keyword. Possible keywords include

INTEGER
REAL
DOUBLE PRECISION
COMPLEX
LOGICAL

A typical TYPE declaration statement could be

DOUBLE PRECISION A, B, I, IT

where the variable names A, B, I, and IT are assigned as double precision variables. Notice that the rule for naming integer variables has been negated for the names I and IT. However, any other integer variable names will be considered to represent integers unless otherwise declared. When a variable name appears in a TYPE declaration statement, the statement must precede the use of the variable in another statement. Furthermore, a variable can only be specified once in a given program. Some examples of TYPE declaration statements are as follows:

(a) INTEGER   ALL, OF, THIS, STUFF
    The variables in the list become integer variables.
(b) DOUBLE PRECISION   BIG, NUM, BERS
    The variables in the list are treated as double precision variables.
(c) COMPLEX   CON, JUG, ATE, PAIRS
    The variables listed refer to complex variables and can only take on complex number values.
(d) LOGICAL   BOOL, EAN, DATA
    The variables in the list are declared to be logical variables and can have only a value of .TRUE. or .FALSE.

The terms variable and constant in FORTRAN do not have precisely the same meaning as the algebraic variable and constant. For example, in the quadratic expression $ax^2 + bx + c = y$, the x and y are algebraic variables and the a, b, and c are constants, whereas in FORTRAN the x and y could be variables and the a, b, and c could also be variables. If the quadratic expression were written

$10.0x^2 + 3.0x - 5.0 = y$

the quantities would still have the same algebraic significance, whereas in FORTRAN the x and y would be variables and the numbers would be constants.

2-3. FORTRAN EXPRESSIONS AND STATEMENTS.

A FORTRAN arithmetic statement has the general form $X = Y$, where X is the name of a variable and Y is an expression, variable, or constant. An expression or arithmetic expression in FORTRAN is a sequence of variables and/or constants separated by arithmetic symbols that define the mathematical operations to be made. The symbols representing the arithmetic operations appear below.

Symbol	Operation
+	addition
−	subtraction
*	multiplication
/	division
**	exponentiation
=	equality (This symbol does not have the same meaning as algebraic equality.)

In the FORTRAN language, the arithmetic symbols express arithmetic operations in a manner completely analogous to the algebraic expression of arithmetic operations. For example, $(X + Y)*Z**2$ in FORTRAN is equivalent to the algebraic expression $(x + y)z^2$, and $(X - Y/W)**A$ in FORTRAN is equivalent to the algebraic expression $(x - y/w)^a$. In FORTRAN the arithmetic operation symbols can never be omitted when forming an expression, as they can in algebra. For example, in algebra the expression xy indicates the product of x and y, but in FORTRAN this must be written $X*Y$. When constants are used in an expression, they will have definite numerical values; but the value of a variable must be defined prior to the use of the variable name in an expression. In a FORTRAN statement such as $VOL = (XMOLES*0.0821*TEMP)/PRESS$, in order for VOL to be evaluated, values for the variables XMOLES, TEMP, and PRESS must have been previously established somewhere in the program. In other words, calculations cannot be carried out unless values for all the factors involved in the calculations have been defined. The values may be established by arithmetic statements or by input statements. These types of statements will be discussed in Section 2-6.

Certain rules must be followed when forming a FORTRAN expression.

1. All quantities separated by a +, −, *, or / must be of the same form or mode; that is, they must be either real or integer. In the FORTRAN language, mixed mode in most arithmetic expressions is not allowed. Thus real and integer variables and constants cannot appear in the same arithmetic expression. Some examples of invalid arithmetic expressions are

X∗2, (J − 1.3)∗Z, I + 3 + L − 1.0E2, (THIS + THAT)/INTG, MEAN − X1

Some FORTRAN IV compilers allow mixed-mode expressions (see rule 7). However, in FORTRAN II it is important to ensure that all arithmetic expressions are free from mixed mode.

2. Real numbers (variable or constant) may be raised to real or integer powers. Because of the way in which arithmetic statements are converted to machine-executable code, a real constant or variable may be raised to an integer or real power. Generally an integer power is desirable and should be used whenever possible. However, the integer power cannot normally be a fraction. Some examples of arithmetic expression involving exponentiation are

(1./2.)∗FMASS∗VEL∗∗2
XML∗(V1/V2)∗∗4
A∗X∗∗3 + B∗X∗∗2 + C∗X + D

The expression (3.0∗R∗T/GPM)∗∗(1/2) is not valid, for it contains an integer exponent that will give an incorrect result. This is because 1/2 in integer arithmetic is 0. A valid form of the above expression could be (3.0∗R∗T/GPM)∗∗(1./2.). Double precision variables and constants can also be raised to real or integer powers. However, integer and complex variables and constants can only be raised to integer powers.

3. Spaces and parentheses may be employed to make an expression more legible. It is sometimes convenient to place blank spaces and parentheses in expressions so that they may be more easily checked for errors. For example, the expression A∗X∗∗2+B∗X+C can be more easily read if blank spaces are used: A∗X∗∗2 + B∗X + C. The expression X−Y∗Z∗∗3+3.0/Y can be more clearly written as X − Y∗Z∗∗3 + 3.0/Y. Parentheses can be used to enclose any portion of the expression for clarity or for the necessary definition of the intended arithmetic operations. The two preceding examples could be written as A∗(X∗∗3) + (B∗X) + C and X − (Y∗(Z∗∗3)) + (3.0/Y) so that they can be read more easily. When ambiguity occurs in an expression, parentheses are used to clarify the expression so that the correct operations are carried out. The expression X∗Y∗∗Z∗A + 2.0 can be written as ((X)∗(Y∗∗Z)∗A) + 2.0 if this is intended. The ambiguous expression X + Y/Z + 2.0E3 may be written (X + Y)/(Z + 2.0E3) if this is intended, or as X + (Y/Z) + 2.0E3 if this is intended. To express PV/RT, we must write P∗V/(R∗T), or (P/R)∗(V/T), but not P∗V/R∗T. To express $X^{Y+.1}$, we must write X∗∗(Y + .1) and not X∗∗Y + .1. The power, in this case, must be enclosed in parentheses.

4. The order of arithmetic operations followed when an expression is evaluated is the same order followed in algebra. This order of operations is exponentiation, followed by multiplication and division from left to right, followed by addition and subtraction from left to right. The order of operations for the expression A∗X∗∗2 + B∗X − C/Y is as follows:

(a) X^2 is calculated	exponentiation
(b) X^2 is multiplied by A	multiplication from left ⎫ multiplication
(c) X is multiplied by B	next multiplication from ⎪ and
	left ⎬ division from
	⎪ left to right
(d) C is divided by Y	division on right ⎭
(e) BX is added to AX^2	addition from left ⎫ addition and
(f) C/Y is subtracted from $AX^2 + BX$	subtraction on right ⎬ subtraction from
	⎭ left to right

5. The order of operations may be altered by use of parentheses. The operations within a set of parentheses are carried out according to normal order. The quantities within the parentheses will be evaluated before being used as part of the overall expression. In the expression (A + B)/(C∗D), the sequence of operations is as follows:

(a) C is multiplied by D.
(b) B is added to A.
(c) The sum, A + B, is divided by the product CD.

In the expression ((C + X/Y)/((A∗∗2) − D))∗∗.5, the values within the inner parentheses are first determined according to the normal order of operations, then the value of quantities within the outer parentheses is determined, and, finally, the square root of the result is determined. When writing an arithmetic expression, any number of parentheses may be used to express the correctly intended operations.

6. No two arithmetic symbols can be used in sequence. To avoid placing two arithmetic operators next to one another, parentheses may be used to separate the symbols. For example, the expression X/−Y should be written as X/(−Y), and the expression X∗−Y∗∗2 should be written as X∗(−Y∗∗2).

7. As mentioned, some FORTRAN IV compilers allow mixed-mode arithmetic statements. These compilers are designed to convert all constants and variables to the same form according to specific hierarchy. The hierarchy normally followed is complex, double precision, real, and integer. Thus, if an expression contains a complex quantity, the expression is evaluated as a complex quantity. If no complex quantity is present but a double precision quantity is present, the expression is evaluated in double precision form. The overall evaluated form of a mixed-mode expression depends on the highest level variable or constant that appears. Several compilers allow only a certain amount of mixed mode, such as real and double precision or real and complex. It should be emphasized that mixed-mode expressions are not common, nor even desirable, in most programs.

As stated previously, the general form of a FORTRAN arithmetic statement is X = Y. The equal sign in FORTRAN is not intended to convey the algebraic meaning of a state of equality; it is used to indicate the action of setting equal. That is, the equal sign instructs the computer, when execution of the statement occurs, to replace or establish the value of the variable to the left of the equal sign with the value of the constant, variable, or evaluated expression on the right of the equal sign. An arithmetic statement may be used merely to establish a value for a variable when desired, a simple but important use. For example,

    I = 1
    SUM = 0.0
    AN = 6.02E23
    R = 0.0821
    JCOUNT = 0

Another form of this type of statement is one in which a variable is given the value of another variable.

    AVE = X
    RESULT = SUM
    I = JKL
    FMEAN = XSUM
    ID = NUM
    THIS = THAT

Remember that the equal sign results in the value of the right-hand term being assigned to the variable name on the left. This will replace the previous value of the left-hand variable or initialize a value for it. Furthermore, the variable on the right will not have its value altered or destroyed by using it in such an expression. Since the equality sign does not have the normal algebraic meaning, we can write statements having the same variable name on both sides of the equal sign. This allows us to alter or increment the value of any variable. For example, the statement $X = X + 1.0$ means that 1.0 is to be added to the existing value of X and the resulting value is to be assigned to the variable name X. The statement $I = I + 1$ would have a similar meaning involving the integer variable I. The statement THIS = THIS*THIS + THAT will result in the value of THIS being squared and then added to the value of THAT. Then the resulting value is assigned to the variable name THIS. This capability allows us to alter the value of the variable when desired and then use the same variable name to refer to the new value. In other words, the value of a variable may be varied.

   Another important use of the arithmetic statement is that it can convert an integer variable into a real variable or vice versa. This is possible because the mode of the right-hand part of the statement will be converted to the mode of the left-hand variable before the value is assigned to the variable name. Of course, this only occurs when the modes on the two sides of the equal sign differ. For example, the statement $X = I$ results in the integer value of I being converted to a real quantity and then assigned as the value of X. However, remember that the value for I is still retained. This conversion from integer to real changes the form in which the value is stored in the computer. Normally, more memory-core locations are used for a real value than for an integer value. This ability to convert an integer variable to a real variable is useful when the value of an integer variable is to be applied in a calculation involving real quantities. The statement I = X results in the integer portion of X being assigned to the integer variable name I. In this situation, the digits to the right of the decimal point in the value of the real variable are lost (truncated). Although seldom used, this type of arithmetic statement is very convenient when needed.

The most powerful use of the arithmetic statement is to define a series of arithmetic operations, involving variables and constants, that are to be carried out and the result assigned to a specific variable name. Any normal algebraic expression can be written in the form of a FORTRAN arithmetic statement as long as the algebraic expression is rearranged so that one variable is to the left of the equal sign—only one variable symbol can appear on the left. Once the algebraic statement has been rearranged in the acceptable form, the portion to the right of the equal sign can be converted to a FORTRAN expression. Some examples of algebraic expressions and equivalent FORTRAN statements follow.

1. The equation of state of an ideal gas is given by $PV = nRT$. When solved for P, we obtain $P = nRT/V$. A FORTRAN arithmetic statement would be

P = (XMOLES*0.0821*TEMP)/VOL

2. Van der Waals equation of state for a gas is

$$\left(P + \frac{an^2}{V^2}\right) V - nb = nRT.$$

When solved for P, we obtain

$$P = \frac{nRT}{V - nb} - \frac{an^2}{V^2}.$$

A FORTRAN arithmetic statement of this is

PRESS = ((FN*R*T)/(V − FN*B)) − ((A*FN**2)/(V**2))

3. Kinetic energy can be expressed as $KE = \frac{1}{2}mv^2$. FORTRAN statements for this could be

EKIN = (XM/2.0)*(V**2)

or

EKIN = .5*XM**2

or

EKIN = (1./2.)*XM*(V**2)

4. Dalton's law of partial pressures involving three components can be written as $P_t = P_a + P_b + P_c$. As a FORTRAN statement, this would be

PT = PA + PB + PC

5. The expression for the energy of an electron in an atom, according to the Bohr model, is

$$E = \frac{-2\pi^2 m e^4}{n^2 h^2}.$$

In FORTRAN this can be expressed as

EN = ((−2.)*(3.14**2)*XM*(E**4))/((FN**2)*(H**2))

6. In thermodynamics, an expression for the change in enthalpy at given conditions is

$$\Delta H = \Delta E + P \, \Delta V.$$

A FORTRAN statement could be

DELH = DELE + P*DELV

7. The density of a substance at a given temperature is defined as mass per unit volume. This can be expressed in FORTRAN as D = FMASS/VOL.

8. The algorithm for the solution of a quadratic equation is given by

$$x = \frac{-b \pm (b^2 - 4ac)^{1/2}}{2a}.$$

An equivalent FORTRAN statement is not possible because the plus or minus relationship cannot be expressed. However, two FORTRAN statements can be written to represent each case. For example,

X = ((−B) + (B**2 − 4.*A*C)**.5)/(2.*A)

and

X = ((−B) − (B**2 − 4.*A*C)**.5)/(2.*A)

9. The standard deviation may be calculated by

$$s = \left[\frac{\sum x^2 - \frac{(\sum x)^2}{n}}{n - 1} \right]^{1/2}.$$

An analogous FORTRAN arithmetic statement could be

S = (((SUMX2) − (SUMX**2)/FN)/(FN − 1.0))**.5

The variable names SUMX2 and SUMX are used for $\sum x^2$ and $\sum x$ and must be previously calculated before appearing in the statement.

Rather than use an arithmetic statement to establish an initial value for each variable where an initial value is required, most FORTRAN IV compilers allow for such initialization in one statement—the DATA statement. The general form of the DATA statement is

DATA list/$c_1, c_2, \ldots, c_n$/

where DATA is a keyword indicating the initialization of variables, list is a sequence of variable names separated by commas, and the *c* values enclosed within the slashes are the desired values of the list variables. Once initialized in a DATA statement, a variable can be used in any arithmetic expression. Of course, the value of the variable may be altered in some statement following the DATA statement. That is, the variable is not required to retain the initial value indefinitely. A typical DATA statement could be

DATA X1, X2, Y, Z, ICK/12.3, 5.2E5, 10.9, 0.0, 2/

This statement serves the same function and is equivalent to the following arithmetic statements:

X1 = 12.3
X2 = 5.2E5
Y = 10.9
Z = 0.0
ICK = 2

When double precision, complex, or logical variables are initialized in a DATA statement, the list variables must have been previously established in a TYPE declaration statement. For example, consider the following set of statements:

COMPLEX X
DOUBLE PRECISION Y, Z
LOGICAL L
DATA A, B, X, Y, Z, L/4.3, 0.0, (3.7, −5.3), 1.234567891011,
    0.0D00, .TRUE./*

Any logical variable may be initialized in one of the forms: .TRUE., T, .FALSE., or F. The use of logical variables in expressions is discussed below. In FORTRAN IV, the DATA statement is a convenient way to establish initial values of variables. Remember that it is not always necessary to use a DATA statement, for one or more arithmetic statements can accomplish the same objective.

Since FORTRAN IV allows for the manipulation of logical quantities, it is possible to construct a logical statement of the form L = B, where L is a logical variable and B is a logical variable, logical constant, or logical expression. A logical expression is any sequence of constants, variables, and/or arithmetic expressions connected by operation symbols. The expression has a value that depends on the components and the operations; this value can only be .TRUE. or .FALSE.. The operation symbols used in logical expressions are of two types: relational operators and logical operators. The relational operators permit the comparison of numerical data from a logical point of view. That is, two numbers do have a certain relationship as specified by the operator or they do not have this relationship. The result of a relational operation is either .TRUE. or .FALSE.. Six relational operators are available in FORTRAN IV.

---

* Normally such a statement would appear on a single line. It is expressed in this manner because of the space limitations of the printed page.

Operator Keyword Symbol	Meaning
.GT.	greater than
.GE.	greater than or equal to
.EQ.	equal to
.NE.	not equal to
.LE.	less than or equal to
.LT.	less than

The relational operators, which must include the set of periods, can be used to express the .TRUE. or .FALSE. relationship between any two integer variables or constants, real variables or constants, and/or any arithmetic statement. For example, the expression

X .LE. 1.2

will have a value of .TRUE. if X is less than or equal to 1.2 or a value of .FALSE. if X is greater than 1.2. The expression

X + .005 .EQ. TEST

is .TRUE. if the value of the expression X + .005 is equal to the value of TEST and is .FALSE. if the value of the expression is not equal to TEST.

In addition, FORTRAN IV provides a set of logical operators that can be used to evaluate the logical relationships between logical quantities. These operators can combine several logical expressions into a more complex expression.

Operator Keyword Symbol	Use	Significance Value of the expression is true if
.NOT.	.NOT. v	v has the value .FALSE.
.AND.	v .AND. w	the values of v and w are .TRUE.
.OR.	v .OR. w	the value of v or w is .TRUE. or both values are .TRUE.

The terms v and w are logical constants, variables, or expressions. If a logical expression is used with the operator .NOT., it must be enclosed in parentheses in order to define the expression upon which the .NOT. is to operate. As an example of a logical expression, consider the following expression:

Y − X .LE. 100. .OR. KOUNT .GT. 50

The value of the expression is .TRUE. if the value of Y − X is less than or equal to 100 or if the value of KOUNT is greater than 50; otherwise the value of the expression is .FALSE.. Since compound logical expressions can involve arithmetic, relational, and logical operations, a hierarchy of operations has been established: (1) arithmetic (with corresponding internal hierarchy), (2) relational (no internal hierarchy), and (3) logical in the order .NOT., .AND., and .OR.. Sets of parentheses can be used as in arithmetic expressions to override the normal hierarchy of operators. When a logical variable is used in a logical expression, it must have been previously described as a logical variable in a TYPE declaration statement and must have an established value.

As stated previously, the general form of a logical statement in FORTRAN is

L = B

where L is a previously declared logical variable and B has the significance discussed above. When a logical statement is executed, the value of B is determined and assigned as the value of L. Of course, since L is a logical variable, it may only assume the value .TRUE. or the value .FALSE.. In the following examples of logical statements, the logical variables are assumed to have been declared in a TYPE declaration statement in each case.

X = .TRUE.

This statement serves as an initialization of the variable X.

DATA A, B, C/T, T, T/
LOGIC = A .AND. .NOT. (B .AND. C)

The validity of the expression depends on the values of the logical variables established in the DATA statement. The expression is evaluated using these values, and the result is assigned to the logical variable LOGIC. Confirm that the value of the above expression is .FALSE..

BOOL = (X1 − X2) .LT.(1.0E−4) .OR.(NTALLY) .GT.(100)

The value of BOOL is .TRUE. if either or both of the relational expressions is .TRUE.. The parentheses are added for clarity and are not actually required.

An extensive explanation of the use of logical statements is beyond the scope of this book. However, as we shall see in several example programs discussed later, logical expressions can be quite useful for certain decision-making processes.

2-4. CODING FORTRAN STATEMENTS.

A FORTRAN program consists of a series of FORTRAN statements arranged to accomplish a given objective. The normal procedure followed when devising a program is to develop a flow chart for the program and then write statements corresponding to the parts of the flow chart. The programmer can write the FORTRAN statements on a FORTRAN coding sheet from which the statements can be keypunched into cards. An example of a coding form with some statements is shown in Figure 2-1. The statements shown are not intended to comprise a program but only to illustrate statement coding. Of course, any convenient sheet of paper can be used for coding if a form is not available. Each line on the form consists of 72 columns corresponding to the first 72 columns of a punched card. When the program is punched on cards, it will be punched according to the way in which it is written on the coding form. Each line of the form corresponds to one card. Each FORTRAN statement may have an identi-

IBM   FORTRAN CODING FORM

Punching Instructions						Card Form #		Page	of
Program EXAMPLE			Graphic							Identification
Programmer	Date		Punch							73 80

C FOR COMMENT

STATEMENT NUMBER	C	FORTRAN STATEMENT

```
C THIS IS A COMMENT

  2  X = Y

     A = (X + Y)/Z

 20  ANSWER = A + B + C + D + E + F + G + H + XI + XJ + XK + XL + XM +
  1  XN + XM + O + P + Q + R + S + T + U + V + W + X + Y + Z
```

FIG. 2-1. FORTRAN coding form.

fying number associated with it, as shown in the figure. This number is called a statement number and can be from one to four digits in length. Columns 2 through 5 of the coding form or the corresponding punched card are reserved for statement numbers. Any statement may have a statement number; however, only statements that must be referenced in some other part of the program need statement numbers. Consequently, it is preferable to assign statement numbers only to statements that must be referenced by the program or the programmer. Any digits can be used for statement numbers and no numerical order is needed, but no two statements in a given program should have the same statement numbers.

The FORTRAN statements can be written only in columns 7 through 72 of a given line, and only one statement can be written on a given line. If a statement exceeds the 66 characters available on a given line, it may be continued on the next line. The continuation is noted by writing a nonzero digit in column 6 of the continuation line. Whenever a continuation of a statement is necessary, one or more continuation lines can be used as long as column 6 of the continuation lines contains a digit. The number of continuation lines or continuation cards allowed depends on the type of compiler, but generally the number is sufficient for most purposes. The continuation method is illustrated in Figure 2-1.

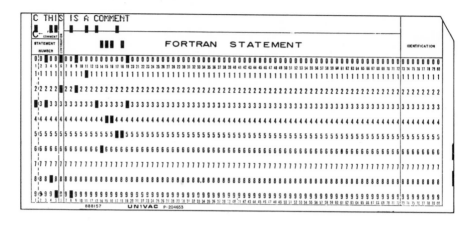

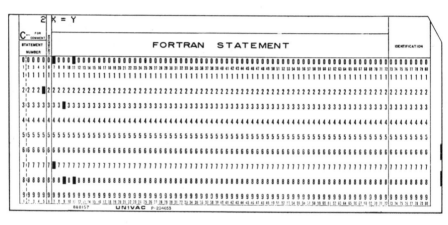

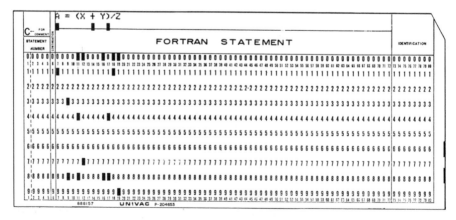

FIG. 2-2. Punched cards with FORTRAN statements.

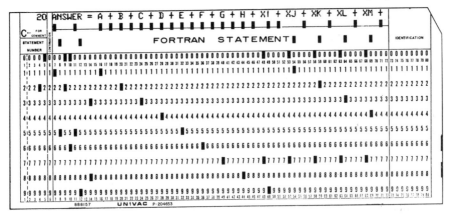

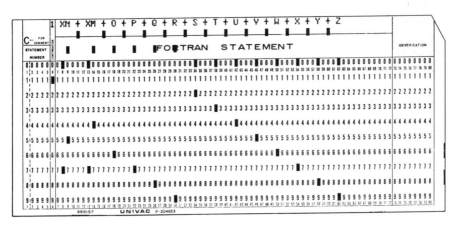

Fig. 2-2 (continued)

Any line or card with a C in column 1 serves as a comment card and is not considered a source statement by the compiler. Comment cards, which explain or give commentary on parts of the program for reference purposes, do not affect the program in any way, for they are not compiled. Their significance lies in the fact that they are included in any printed listing of the source program. Numerous comment cards are useful in a program when it is to be read by persons other than the programmer. A comment line is shown in Figure 2-1. Columns 73 to 80 of the punched cards may be used by the programmer for sequencing or identification purposes. These columns are not processed by the compiler. Figure 2-2 shows some punched FORTRAN cards containing the statements from the coding form in Figure 2-1. As many blank spaces as are convenient or needed for clarity can be used on the punched card. The FORTRAN compiler disregards extra blank spaces when used to separate parts of the statement. The methods involved in arranging the source statements for processing by the computer are discussed in Appendix 2.

2-5. FORTRAN ROUTINES.

A routine in FORTRAN can be considered a sequence of statements set up to accomplish some desired computation. A routine may be part of a larger program designed to solve a specific type of problem. After the approach to setting up the program has been flow charted or defined, a good way to write the program is to develop routines for each of the separate phases of the problem and then connect these routines logically. A routine can be a set of statements that will result in the calculation of a value for a given variable or set of variables. Usually the routine will consist of steps that establish the values for certain variables (initialization), followed by steps that accomplish calculations using the variables. Keep in mind that the writing of FORTRAN statements merely serves to define the logical solution process and, in order for execution of the statements to take place, they must be read into the computer and translated to machine code. Some routines, such as those to find the square root or logarithm of a number, are used so frequently in FORTRAN programs that they are included as part of the compiler and can be employed by the programmer when desired. These prewritten routines are called subroutines and will be discussed later (Chapter 4).

To illustrate, consider the calculation of the volume of a given number of moles of a gas at a given temperature and pressure using the ideal gas equation, $PV = nRT$. The routine can consist of establishing the values for the variables, followed by a statement that accomplishes the calculation of the volume. A possible sequence of statements could be

```
PATM = 1.200
TKELV = 25.0 + 273.
XMOLES = 2.32E−2
VOLUME = (XMOLES*.0821*TKELV)/PATM
```

Another example of a routine is a case in which the percentage water in a hydrate is calculated from experimental data. The experimental data are collected in the laboratory by heating weighed samples of hydrate to drive off the water and then determining the mass of the residue. A sequence of statements that will provide for the calculation of the percentage by mass water is as follows:

```
HYDRT = 2.1823
ANHYD = 1.8213
PH20 = ((HYDRT − ANHYD)/HYDRT)*100.
```

Suppose the experiment referred to above were carried out three times, so that three sets of data were collected. In that case we would need a routine to calculate the average percent by mass water in the hydrate.

```
HYDRT1  = 2.0035
ANHYD1  = 1.7863
HYDRT2  = 3.2704
ANHYD2  = 2.7342
HYDRT3  = 2.7248
ANHYD3  = 2.2704
FNUM    = 3.0
PH201   = ((HYDRT1 − ANHYD1)/HYDRT1)∗100.
PH202   = ((HYDRT2 − ANHYD2)/HYDRT2)∗100.
PH203   = ((HYDRT3 − ANHYD3)/HYDRT3)∗100.
AVEPC   = (PH201 + PH202 + PH203)/FNUM
```

Note that the last five statements are generally written and could be used to calculate the average percentage for any group of three sets of experimental data. New sets of data could be introduced by redefining the data variables that comprise the first six statements in the above routine.

2-6. INPUT AND OUTPUT STATEMENTS.

By writing a sequence of statements, we can establish routines to accomplish a wide variety of arithmetic computations. However, once results have been calculated, obviously it is desirable to have some way to record them on some output media. Furthermore, it would be desirable to make routines more generally applicable by providing for the input of numerical values for variables via some input device. FORTRAN allows for both possibilities by providing for the formation of input/output statements. Input/output statements can be formed to allow for the reading in or the output of information from the computer in a predefined form. It is important to note that these types of statements cannot be used unless the nature (magnitudes and modes) of the data is precisely defined. There is no way for the computer to know whether the information to be input is integer, or real, or even alphabetic, how many digits each number has, where the decimal point is located, or how the information is spaced on the input medium. A complete description of the data must be provided in a coded form. Furthermore, a detailed description of the desired form of output must be supplied by appropriate codes. The precise definition of the forms of data is accomplished by means of the FORMAT statement, which will be discussed later (Section 2-7).

In FORTRAN II, an input statement has the general form read *n*, list. In this statement, read refers to a specific keyword (verb) indicating the type of input device to be used, *n* is the statement number of the FORMAT statement, and list consists of a sequence of variable names separated by commas, the values of which are to be read in from the input device. The values that are read in are assigned to the variable names in the list. When the input device is the card reader, the keyword used is READ. An example of an input statement using the card reader is

READ 10, A, VEL, I

This results in a card or cards being read, and the values, which appear on the cards according to the form described by the FORMAT statement numbered 10, are assigned to the variable names in the list. Thus the values for the variables may be initialized or varied by reading data cards. In many cases, this is a more desirable way to establish a value for a variable than the use of an arithmetic statement written into the program. This is especially true when a program is written so as to be as generally applicable as possible. When the typewriter is used for input, the keyword used is ACCEPT. An example of an ACCEPT input statement is

ACCEPT 20, X1, IN, COUNT, KLM

This statement results in values being read in from the typewriter in the form described by the FORMAT statement numbered 20 and assigned to the variable names in the list. This type of statement would normally be used only when the programmer is actually operating the computer or had control of the computer from a remote console. The keywords READ INPUT TAPE n are used when magnetic tape is used. The n refers to the code number of the tape device used (normally this is 5). An example of a statement that provides for input from magnetic tape is

READ INPUT TAPE 3, 4, X, Y, Z, X0, X1, X2, X3, NUM

This statement results in the values for the variables in the list being read from magnetic tape, contained in the tape-drive device with code number 3, according to the description given by FORMAT statement number 4. This type of input statement is commonly employed for programs written for large computers with magnetic tape input.

The general form of an output statement in FORTRAN II is write n, list, where write refers to a keyword that indicates the output device to be used, and n is the statement number of the FORMAT statement that defines the output form of the values of the variables named in the list. The keywords used are TYPE for typewriter output, PRINT for printer output, PUNCH for punched card output, and WRITE OUTPUT TAPE n (n is usually 6) for magnetic tape output. Some examples of FORTRAN output statements are

TYPE 100, THIS, THAT, RESULT, NIX, OHBOY

This causes the existing values of the variables in the list to be typed out in a form described by the FORMAT statement numbered 100.

PUNCH 56, ALL, THE, GOOD, ANS, I, HOPE

According to this statement, the values for the variables in the list are to be punched on a card or cards according to the description given by FORMAT statement 56.

PRINT 2666, FACTS, AND, HALF, TRUTHS

When the computer has an on-line printer, this statement results in the printing of the values of the variables according to the description given by FORMAT statement 2666. With some computers, if there is no on-line printer, the PRINT keyword is considered synonymous with the keyword TYPE.

WRITE OUTPUT TAPE 4, 26, EVERY, THING, SIG, NIF, ICANT

This statement calls for the recording of the values of the variables in the list on magnetic tape, contained on the tape drive with code number 4, according to the specifications given in the FORMAT statement 26. The particular input and output devices used by a programmer will depend on the type of computer.

In FORTRAN IV, each of the input and output devices is assigned a code number, called a logical unit number. Instead of using a specific keyword to specify the input device, only one keyword, plus the logical unit number specifying the device, is required. The general form of a FORTRAN IV input statement is

READ (m,n) list

where READ is the keyword indicating input, m is the logical unit number specifying the input device, and n is the number of the FORMAT statement that specifies the form of the variables in the list. The numerical codes used for the logical unit numbers are normally one-digit integers. The particular numbers used may vary for different computer installations. Typical logical unit numbers for input may be

Logical Unit Number	Input Device
1	magnetic tape drive 1
2	magnetic tape drive 2
3	magnetic tape drive 3
4	magnetic tape drive 4
5	card reader

Some examples of FORTRAN IV input statements are

READ (5, 10) A, B, C
READ (4, 1) X1, X2, I1, I2
READ (5, 200) DATA, N, CONST, INT

FORTRAN IV output statements use only one keyword along with the appropriate logical unit number indicating the output device to be used. The general form of the FORTRAN IV output statement is

WRITE (m,n) list

where WRITE is the keyword indicating output, m is the logical unit number specifying the output device, and *n* is the number of the FORMAT statement that specifies the form of the variables in the list. Typical logical unit numbers used for output purposes are

Logical Unit Number	Output Device
1	magnetic tape drive 1
2	magnetic tape drive 2
3	magnetic tape drive 3
4	magnetic tape drive 4
6	printer
7	card punch

Some examples of FORTRAN IV output statements are

WRITE (6, 200) THIS, ANS

WRITE (2, 60) WHATS, HAP, PEN, NING, BABY

In FORTRAN IV, all input and output statements will have the keywords discussed above and will utilize the logical unit numbers assigned to the particular computer installation. Remember that the logical unit number and the FORMAT statement number must be included in parentheses separated by a comma, and all the list variables must be separated by commas. However, no comma is needed immediately in front of the first list variable. The two FORTRAN input statements

READ *n*, list

and

READ (5, *n*) list

and the two output statements

PRINT *n*, list

and

WRITE (6, *n*) list

accomplish the same operations. The first statement of each pair is a FORTRAN II statement, while the second statement of each pair is a FORTRAN IV statement. However, some FORTRAN IV compilers are designed so that either form of these input and output statements can be used in FORTRAN IV programs.

To increase the speed and efficiency of processing computer programs, punched cards are first recorded on magnetic tape. The magnetic tape containing the magnetically recorded equivalent of many program cards and data cards can then be read into the computer at a much faster rate than a card reader can function. Each card recorded on magnetic tape is called a tape record. When data for a compiled program are to be read in from magnetic tape, an appropriate READ statement using the proper code number for the input tape drive must be included in the program. The READ statement can be used to input one or more tape records of data cards, the number of tape records read depending on the specifications given in the FORMAT statement corresponding to the READ statement. It should be pointed out that the input of source statements by magnetic tape is a process that is not controlled by the programmer in his program but by the computer operator. The programmer can only provide for magnetic tape input of previously recorded data.

Magnetic tape can also be used for output of calculated results of a program. Once the results have been recorded on magnetic tape, they can be converted into printed or punched information on a smaller computer. Since magnetic tape output is much faster than other forms of output, magnetic tape recording and printing of information via a smaller computer can save significant amounts of processing time on a large computer. The output of information is accomplished by means of a WRITE statement with the proper code number for the output tape drive. If output is to be printed at a later time, the FORMAT statement referred to by the WRITE statement must contain the proper printer control characters. (See Hollerith specifications in Section 2-7, which discusses printer control characters.) The programmer should obtain information from the computing facility concerning the availability of magnetic tape input and output and the code numbers used for the input tape drive and the output tape drive.

2-7. FORMAT STATEMENTS AND SPECIFICATIONS.

As noted above, whenever an input or output statement is used, it must refer to some FORMAT statement that defines the nature of the variables in the list. The FORMAT statement must specify the exact size, mode, and location of the variable. Since these specifications must indicate the exact form of input or output information desired, they must be carefully written. FORMAT statements have this general form:

n FORMAT (specifications of list variables)

Here n is an identifying statement number of from one to four digits that allows for referencing by input/output statements. The keyword FORMAT indicates that the information enclosed in the parentheses gives the exact specifications for the list variables in a coded form. The codes used to indicate the nature of the variables are called specification codes or specification modes. Since there are several types of variables—that is, integer, real, complex, double precision, and logical—a specific specification code is used to specify each type. The code letter I refers to integer quantities for input/output purposes. When used in a FORMAT statement, it forms an I specification. I specifications have the general form Iw. The I indicates that the quantity referred to is integer and the w is a number indicating the number of spaces (digits and sign) occupied by the quantity. If the quantity is negative, a minus sign will precede the high-order digit. Since the sign occupies a space, it must be included in the w count along with the number of digits comprising the quantity. The use of I specifications for output purposes and for input purposes differs; consequently, it is convenient to consider the two cases separately. When I specification is used for output in the form Iw, the *w* digit refers to the number of spaces to be occupied by the number on the output medium. In output, a sign will always accompany the digits of an integer, so *w* must be large enough to permit the recording of the sign and the digits. If *w* is too small, erroneous output results; if it is too large, leading blanks are supplied. Some examples of I specification for output are

Number	Specification	Recorded Form on Output Medium	
1	I2	bl	(If the sign is plus, a blank precedes the
23	I3	b23	number and no sign is recorded. Remem-
56	I4	bb56	ber that the lower-case b is used here to
1234	I5	b1234	indicate a blank space.)
−6	I2	−6	
−1234	I5	−1234	

When I specification is used for input in the form Iw, the *w* refers to the number of spaces the number occupies on the input medium. The *w* should include the space occupied by the sign if it is present on the input medium. A positive value is assumed if no sign is present. A few examples of I specifications for input are

Form of Number on Input Medium	Specification	
−1234	I5	
1234	I4	
1	I1	
+1	I2	
b12	I3	(The blank is read and con-
−166	I4	sidered to be zero.)

A FORMAT statement using the I specification is demonstrated in the following routine:

```
    READ 10, INTG, KOUNT
 10 FORMAT(I4, I5)
    PUNCH 10, INTG, KOUNT
```

This routine results in a data card being read to obtain the values of INTG and KOUNT; then the values are punched out on a card. According to the FORMAT statement, the values for INTG and KOUNT are located on the data card in card columns 1 through 4 and 5 through 9, respectively. Further-more, since the PUNCH statement uses the same FORMAT statement as the READ statement, the values of the integer variables are to be punched out in the same form in which they were read.

The code letter E refers to real numbers with exponents. E specification for output has the general form Ew.d. The E is the code letter signifying the real with exponent mode, *w* is the number of spaces to be occupied by the number, including four spaces for the exponent (one for the E, one for the sign, and two for the two-digit exponent), one space for the decimal point, and one space for the sign. The d is a number indicating the number of digits desired to the right of the decimal point, that is, the position of the decimal point. When this specification is used, it provides for output having a mantissa w-6 digits long with a sign (blank for a plus) and a properly positioned decimal point. The mantissa is followed by the letter E and a signed two-digit characteristic. A few examples of E specification for output are as follows:

Number	Specification	Recorded Form on Output Medium	
−12.1234	E12.6	−.121234E+02	
123.	E10.3	b1.230E+02	(An extra zero is recorded,
−1.23	E9.2	−1.23E−00	since 4 digits were specified.)
6.023×10^{23}	E10.3	b6.023E+23	
1.2345678	E14.8	b.12345678E+01	
.12345678	E14.7	b1.2345678E−01	(This is the specification for the standard scientific notation form of a number.)
−12.34	E9.1	−12.3E−00	(A digit is deleted, since only 3 digits were specified.)

An example of E specification in a program is as follows:

        TYPE 200, X
    200 FORMAT(E14.7)

The value of X is to be typed in the standard scientific notation form. When the E specification is used for input data, w specifies the length of the datum, including the sign, if present, the decimal point, if included, and the E with the signed or unsigned exponent. The d value indicates the position of the decimal point. The exponent part of such an E mode number may be shortened when it is punched on a card or recorded on some other input medium. This saves time and space and shortens the w count. For example, E+01, E 01, E01, +01, E+1, E1, or +1 are all valid forms for the exponent corresponding to 10^1. Furthermore, the decimal point need not be included as part of the number in E mode for input. However, for clarity it may be convenient to always write E mode numbers in the standard form. Of course, numbers exceeding the capacity of the F mode (see below) must be written in E form. Some examples of E specification for input are as follows:

Number Recorded on Input Medium	Specification
−1.23E+02	E9.2
b1.2345678E−02	E14.7
+1235E8 (intended meaning 1.235×10^8)	E7.3
−.87654321E16	E13.8
9876+5 (intended meaning 9.876×10^5)	E6.3
b12345678.E−60	E14.0
0.0E−00	E7.1

An example of E specification for input would be

        ACCEPT 2, DATUM
      2 FORMAT(E14.7)

This results in 14 spaces being read for the value of DATUM in the E mode, with 7 digits to the right of the decimal point.

The code letter F refers to real numbers without exponents. The F specification has the form Fw.d. The F indicates that the quantity specified is real, with no exponent, and the w is a digit indicating the number of spaces occupied by the quantity including the sign, if present, and the decimal point. The d is a number indicating the number of digits to the right of the decimal point in the specified quantity. Numbers in F mode are used quite often because many numerical quantities can be more conveniently written in this rather than the E form. When F specification is used for output in the form Fw.d, the w must include a space for the sign (blank if it is positive) and the decimal point. Consequently, the actual number of digits that are output will be $w-2$.

Number	Specification	Recorded Form on Output Medium
12.34	F6.2	b12.34
−1.0	F4.1	−1.0
1.00	F4.1	b1.0
15762.3	F8.1	b15762.3
23.	F5.1	b23.0

In F specification used for input purposes, the w includes the number of spaces occupied by the number on the input medium.

Number Recorded on Input Medium	Specification
+123.456	F8.3
1.2368	F6.4
−123.45678	F10.5
b888.88888	F10.5
b123 (intended value 123.)	F4.0
123456 (intended value .123456)	F6.6

An example of a routine using F specification is as follows:

```
      READ 100, XFACT
  100 FORMAT(F7.3)
      PUNCH 101, XFACT
  101 FORMAT(F8.3)
```

This routine results in the value of XFACT being read from the first 7 columns of a data card and then being punched in the first 8 columns of the output card. The extra column in the punched card could provide for the sign.

When data or other materials are read in or output, it is desirable to be able to allow for spacing on the input or output medium. The code letter X is used in the FORMAT statement specifications to indicate spacing. The X specification has the form wX, where w is a number from one to 50 that indicates the number of spaces. The function of this specification in output is to allow for the skipping of w spaces on the output medium. When used for input, w spaces are skipped on the input medium. The X specification provides for the convenient spacing of data so that input and output quantities can be made more readable. To illustrate X specification for input, consider the following case. A data card such as

bb1.234E8bbb12.67bbbbbbbbbbbbbbbbbb12

is to be read in. This could be accomplished with the statements

    READ 10, X, Y, I
10 FORMAT(2XE7.3, 3XF5.2, 18XI2)

The above FORMAT statement calls for omitting the proper number of spaces so that the values of the variables are read in correctly. Note that commas are not needed after the X specifications. In output processes, the X specification can be used to space the output to make it convenient to read. For example, the statements

    PUNCH 20, Y, X, I
20 FORMAT(F6.2, 30XE10.3, 31XI3)

result in the values of Y, X, and I being punched on a card with the specified number of spaces between each value.

The code letter D is used to refer to double precision quantities (FORTRAN IV only), and the general form of the D specification is Dw.d. The use of the D specification is similar to the use of the E specification except that the number specified usually consists of additional digits. As with output by E specification, the w count for output by D specification must include one space for the sign, one space for the decimal point, one space for the D, and three spaces for the signed two-digit characteristic. Thus the number of digits output will be $w-6$. Some examples of D specification for output follow.

Number	Specification	Recorded Form on Output Medium
12345678.12345678	D22.15	b1.234567812345678D+07
−.0005678900000000	D11.4	−5.6789D−04

For input by D specification, the w count must include all spaces occupied by the number on the input medium. Some examples of input by D specification would be

Number Recorded on Input Medium	Specification
−1.2345678765432D23	D19.13
2.303D−4	D8.3

Since complex numbers are normally stored in the form of two real quantities, the FORMAT specification of complex numbers consists of two E and/or F specifications (FORTRAN IV only). Therefore the same procedures that apply to E and F specifications are used to specify complex quantities. Examples of input specifications for complex numbers include

Form of Complex Number on Input Medium	Specification
+1.3E2−12.7	E6.1, F5.1
2.76b3.20	F4.2, F5.3

Some examples of output specifications for complex numbers are

Complex Number	Specification	Recorded Form on Output Medium
(1.7, −3.72)	F4.1, F5.2	b1.7−3.72
(8.2E5, 4.3E2)	E8.1, E8.1	b8.2E+05b4.3E+02
(1.23E−2, 1.07E−3)	E14.8, E14.8	b.12300000E−01b.10700000E−02

For the input and output of logical variables, the L specification can be used (FORTRAN IV only). L specification has the general form Lw. When used for input, this specification results in w spaces being read from the input medium, and the first T or F encountered will result in .TRUE. or .FALSE. being stored for the logical variable specified. When used for output, the L specification results in a recording of a T or F preceded by $w-1$ spaces. Examples of L specification are

Form on Input Medium	Specification for Input	
bT	L2	

Value of Stored Logical Variable	Specification for Output	Output
.FALSE.	L4	bbbF

Occasionally it is desirable to manipulate alphabetic data internally. The A specification allows for the establishment of alphabetic data as variables that can be processed. The general form of the A specification is Aw, where A is the code letter indicating an alphabetic variable and w is a digit indicating the number of alphabetic characters comprising the variable. Because of the way alphabetic characters are stored in the various computers, the allowable w length

TABLE 2-4. Allowable Alphabetic Variable Lengths

Computer Type	w Length	
	Integer Variable	Real Variable
IBM 360 RCA 70	8	16
CDC 3200 UNIVAC III	4	8
IBM 7000 series	6	6
IBM 1620	2	4
IBM 1400 series	Programmer can assign length.	

often varies for different types of computers. Table 2-4 gives the allowable length for some computers. Alphabetic variable input can be accomplished with such statements as

READ 10, NAME, ALP1, ALP2
10 FORMAT(A2, A4, 5XA4)

or

READ (5, 10) NAME, ALP1, ALP2
10 FORMAT(A2, A4, 5XA4)

These statements result in NAME being assigned the two characters read in from a card, while the variables ALP1 and ALP2 are assigned four characters, each read in from the same card. Once alphabetic variables have been input using A specification, they can be manipulated in the same way that numerical variables are manipulated. However, they are seldom arithmetically manipulated, for this usually serves no purpose. Other types of manipulations, such as rearrangement or output, are common. Alphabetic-variable output could be accomplished with statements such as

PUNCH 20, NAME, ALP1, ALP2
20 FORMAT(A4, A8, A8)

In output, if w exceeds the allowable length, leading blanks are recorded on the output media. Since the allowable w values are rather small, it appears that it is not possible to have a long alphabetic variable that can be referred to by a given name. However, this can be accomplished by certain techniques that will be discussed later.

With input/output statements and accompanying FORMAT statements, routines can be written so that they may be used repeatedly with different sets of data. As a result, routines and programs that are more versatile and generally applicable can be written. Consider the problem involving the calculation of the percentage water in an hydrate discussed in Section 2-4. With input and output statements, the routine given in Section 2-4 can be designed to read data in from cards and to record the results on an output medium. A routine to accomplish this, as well as the calculations, could be

READ 50, HYDRT1, ANHYD1, HYDRT2, ANHYD2, HYDRT3, ANHYD3*
50 FORMAT(F6.4, 1XF6.4)
PH201 = ((HYDRT1 − ANHYD1)/HYDRT1)*100.
PH202 = ((HYDRT2 − ANHYD2)/HYDRT2)*100.
PH203 = ((HYDRT3 − ANHYD3)/HYDRT3)*100.
AVEPC = (PH201 + PH202 + PH203)/3.0
TYPE 60, PH201, PH202, PH203, AVEPC
60 FORMAT(E10.3, 5XE10.3, 5XE10.3, /E10.3)

Notice that in FORMAT 50 the number of specifications is less than the number

---

* It is necessary to print some statements in this form because of the space limitations of the printed page. In programming, statements are always written on a single line unless a continuation line is needed. (See Section 2-4.)

of list variables. If there are more list variables than specifications, then, when the last specification is used, the compiler goes back to the preceding left parenthesis and starts using the specifications again until all the list variables have been specified. However, it is important to note that when the presence of a right parenthesis in a FORMAT specification is detected by the compiler before the list variables have all been specified, a new record, card, or line is used for input or output. Consequently, according to FORMAT 50 above, the values for HYDRT1 and ANHYD1 are read from one card, then a second card is read for the values of HYDRT2 and ANHYD2 in the same form as the previous card, and, finally, a third card is read for the values of HYDRT3 and ANHYD3. This technique is convenient and allows for the punching of one set of experimental data per card. However, if all the data were punched on one card, different FORMAT statements could be used, such as

    50 FORMAT(F6.4, 1XF6.4, 2XF6.4, 1XF6.4, 2XF6.4, 1XF6.4)

or

    50 FORMAT(6F6.4)

In the second example, the statement is designed for the case in which the data are all punched on a card in the same form with no spacing between them. In this case, since the six specifications are the same and the data are next to one another, a 6 can precede the specification to indicate that all six specifications are the same. In general, if specifications of the same type are to be used for data that are side by side, a digit indicating the number of such specifications followed by the specification will suffice.

According to FORMAT 60 in the above routine, the values of the percentages are to be typed on one line with the indicated spacing and then the value of the average percentage is to be typed on a new line. The / symbol is used in the FORMAT statement to indicate that a new record, card, or line is to be used for the variables described by the specifications following the /. The / can be used at any point in an input or output FORMAT specification to indicate that a new record is to be used. That is, it may indicate that a new card is to be read or punched, or that a new line is to be read, typed, or printed. For example, if three variables are to be read from three different cards, we could use the following statements:

    READ 1, X, Y, J
  1 FORMAT(F6.3/E14.8/I5)

The statements

    TYPE 200, INT, A, B, C, D
  200 FORMAT(I5//(E14.8, 5XE14.8/))

result in the value of INT being typed on one line; then the typewriter carriage returns twice; that is, skips to the second line after the line containing INT. Next, the values of A and B are typed, the carriage returns twice—once due to the / and once due to the)—and the values of C and D are typed according to the same format used for A and B.

When writing FORMAT statements for output by the printer, or for magnetic tape that is to be converted to printer output, the first section of the FORMAT specification must contain a printer control statement. This is a statement in code that controls the way in which the printing process occurs. The normal printer control codes and their meanings are

1Hb   skip one line before printing
1H0   skip two lines before printing
1H1   skip to top of new page before printing

For example, the following output statement and accompanying FORMAT statement

    WRITE OUTPUT TAPE 4, 1, X, Y, I, J
  1 FORMAT(1HbF6.3, E14.7, 2I5)

are designed to record the values of X, Y, I, and J on magnetic tape. The FORMAT statement is set up so that when printing of the values is desired, a line will be skipped by the printer before printing occurs. The statements

    PRINT 20, LABEL1, LABEL2, LABEL3, LABEL4
 20 FORMAT(1H1I4)

are set up to print the indicated variables so that each variable is printed on a separate sheet or page of printed output.

Occasionally, in order to clarify and to avoid ambiguity, it is desirable to include, along with the output, a verbal statement describing the nature of the results. The best way to do this is with the H (Hollerith) specification in a FORMAT statement. The H specification makes it possible to place alphanumeric statements or literal constants in the FORMAT statement, thus recording them on the output medium along with the results. An H specification may precede any list specification so that the literal constant will be recorded before the value of the list variable is recorded. The general form is wHliteral constant, where H is the code letter indicating the Hollerith mode (alphanumeric constant mode) and *w* is a number from one to 50 indicating the number of alphanumeric characters, including blanks, that comprise the literal constant. It is important to make sure that the *w* value corresponds precisely to the number of characters and blanks in the constant. Any alphabetic letters, decimal digits, and special characters can be used as part of the literal constant. This H specification provides wide capabilities for the output of commentary with the computed results, but remember that no commentary can be recorded unless it has previously been written into the program. Some examples of FORMAT statements using H specifications are as follows:

236 FORMAT(45HPROGRAM TO CALCULATE PERCENTAGE BY
       MASS WATER)

120 FORMAT(18HTHIS IS AN EXAMPLE)
33 FORMAT(26HLIST OF CALCULATED RESULTS)
44 FORMAT(31HVALUES OF THE FUNCTION Y=X**2+C)
50 FORMAT(4HXSUM, 5X4HYSUM, 5X8HSUM X**2, 5X12HSUM
(X−Y)**2)
57 FORMAT(19HTHE PERCENTAGES ARE, /(E7.3))

Statements like the above provide for commentary and labels for tabular output.

5 FORMAT(4HX = F10.3, 2X4HY = F10.3, 2X6HSUM = E14.8)

Here some H message precedes the specifications for the variables in the list.

17 FORMAT(26HTHE AVERAGE PERCENTAGE IS, F6.2)
1831 FORMAT(11HTHE MEAN = F7.3,/ 25HTHE STANDARD
DEVIATION = E14.7)
200 FORMAT(10H(X+Y)/Z = F7.3, 2X13HTRIAL NUMBER I2)
1852 FORMAT(5HP1 = E14.7, /5HP2 = E14.7, /5HP3 = E14.7)
53 FORMAT(31HEQUIL CONST AS A FUNCTION OF PH,/
(5HPH = E14.7,9H−LOG K = E14.
17,4HK = E14.7)) (This statement was too long for one card, thus
requiring a continuation card.)

Statements similar to the last six statements above provide for descriptive
commentary along with the output of numerical results. The Hollerith mode is
also used at times in an input specification that allows for the variation of the
nature of a literal constant. This technique provides flexibility in the literal
commentary recorded with the results. The H specification can be used to
permit the input of a literal constant from a card or from some other input
medium. Consider the following cases. A data card has the form

CASE NUMBER 2bb10.72bb3.2E5

Statements used to read this card and record the literal constant could be

READ 10, DATUM1, DATUM2
10 FORMAT(13Hbbbbbbbbbbbbbb2XF5.2, 2XE5.1)
5 TYPE 10

These statements result in the first 13 columns of a card being read for a literal
constant, along with the values of DATUM1 and DATUM2. Then the literal
constant is typed out. Note that statement number 5 does not list any variables;
hence only the Hollerith portion of the FORMAT is output.

READ 20
20 FORMAT(25Hbbbbbbbbbbbbbbbbbbbbbbbbb)
PUNCH 20

These statements result in a card being read with a literal constant in the first 25
columns; next, the literal constant is punched in the first 25 columns of a new

card. The card could contain descriptive information like the following name card:

ALFRED E. NEWMAN 1-2-67

2-8. SUBSCRIPTED VARIABLES.

Frequently when a program or routine is designed to accomplish some calculation, it is advisable to repeat the calculation many times with new data. That is, once the routine has been written, it may be advantageous to use it repeatedly with numerous sets of data. In such cases, the data are usually of the same form. Consequently, it would be convenient to represent the data by a specific variable name; but, if it is necessary to retain a series of variable values, they cannot be given the same name. FORTRAN provides the capability of defining a variable in a subscripted form so that the variable name with a specific subscript can be used to refer to a given member of a group of similar data. Any FORTRAN variable may be defined as a subscripted variable having one, two, or three subscripts. That is, the variable may refer to any member of an array or any element of a two- or three-dimensional matrix. A two-dimensional matrix is a rectangular array of numbers in which each number can be referred to by a specific set of subscripts as shown below.

$$
\begin{array}{ccc}
n_{11} & n_{12} & n_{13} \\
n_{21} & n_{22} & n_{23} \\
n_{31} & n_{32} & n_{33}
\end{array}
$$

Matrices are often written so that the numbers are enclosed in brackets or parentheses for notational purposes. For example, the above matrix would be written

$$
\begin{bmatrix}
n_{11} & n_{12} & n_{13} \\
n_{21} & n_{22} & n_{23} \\
n_{31} & n_{32} & n_{33}
\end{bmatrix}
$$

Three-dimensional matrices are analogous to two-dimensional matrices except that they are arrays of numbers arranged in a three-dimensional, rectangular, solid pattern. In order to use a subscripted variable in a program, its maximum size—that is, the maximum value of the subscripts—must be defined by a DIMENSION statement at the beginning of the program. This definition using a DIMENSION statement allows the computer to reserve sufficient storage for all the values of the subscripted variables. The DIMENSION statement has the form:

DIMENSION V1(n), V2(n,n), V3(n,n,n), . . .

Here the keyword DIMENSION indicates that the variable names following it are to be defined as subscripted variables. The names of the subscripted variables are followed by parentheses containing n values, which are numbers indicating the number of subscripts desired. One DIMENSION statement can be used to define as many subscripted variables as can be placed on the first card of the DIMENSION statement and the continuation cards. However, all the names must be separated by commas, and the maximum size of the subscripts must be indicated.

DIMENSION X(10), Y(10,10), IMATRX(5,4,3)

This statement specifies the dimensions of the subscripted variable X(I), which represents the members of an array consisting of ten members, and the subscripted variables Y(I,J) and IMATRX(I,J,K), which represent the members of a 10 by 10 matrix and a 5 by 4 by 3 matrix, respectively. The DIMENSION statement must contain the maximum value of the subscripts so that the compiler can provide storage space for all possible members. However, all the subscripts need not be used in any given situation, but the maximum value of the subscript cannot be exceeded. If the maximum size of the subscripts of a variable is not known, be sure that the entry in the DIMENSION statement is sufficient to accommodate the variable.

DIMENSION XMAT(2, 10), MATRIX(5), X(10, 10, 10), A(5, 5), B(5, 60)
DIMENSION DATA(50), RESULT(50), PERCNT(50), DEV(50)
DIMENSION PRESS(10), VOL(10), TEMP(10), FUNCT(10, 10, 10)

A subscripted variable should only be used in a program when necessary; that is, only when the accumulation and storage of the values of a variable are needed. Unnecessary use of subscripted variables results in waste of computer-core storage. When a subscripted variable is used in an expression on the right or left of an equal sign, the current or desired value of the subscript must be defined by a positive integer quantity. If we let v represent a nonsubscripted integer variable and c and d integer constants, the subscripts of a subscripted variable may be written in one of the following forms:

$$v \quad c \quad v \pm c \quad c*v \quad c*v \pm d$$

When a variable v is used, it must have a previously established value. This fact allows wide flexibility in the assignment of values to the subscripts. The subscripts of a variable used in a statement may be an integer or an integer expression. For example, consider the following statement involving five subscripted variables:

$$P(I) = (X(2, 2, 3) + Y(J + 2))/(Z(2*K, 3)*W(3*J - 2))$$

The subscript of the variable P(I) is the current value of I. The subscript of the variable X(L, M, N) is given by the integers shown. The subscripts of the variables Y(L) and W(L) are determined by the arithmetic operations on the current value of J. The first subscript of the variable Z(L, M) is determined by multiplying the current value of K by 2; the second subscript is given by the integer shown. Remember that whenever an integer variable is used as a subscript, it must have a previously defined value. The statement $X(I) = Y(I)$ results in the current value of $Y(I)$, which depends on the current value of I, being assigned as the value of $X(I)$. The value of I determines the element of $X(I)$ referred to. The statement $X(I) = X(I + 1)$ establishes the value of $X(I)$ to be the same as the value of $X(I + 1)$. The statement $X(I) = Y(I)*X(I)$ replaces the value of element $X(I)$ with the product shown. Notice that in this case all subscripts are the same and are given by the current value of I. The magnitude of the subscript cannot exceed the maximum value defined in the DIMENSION statement. Once a variable has been subscripted, the variable name cannot be used without subscripts in any part of the program except in certain input/output operations. When a subscripted variable is used in a statement, it is important to use the proper value or values for the subscripts. Subscripted variables are quite useful when repeated calculations employing the same routine are being carried out with the members of an array as data. An expression in a routine used repeatedly can have subscripted variables so that the subscripts need only be changed to introduce new data. The percentage calculation in the routine given in Section 2-6 could be made by the statement

$$PH20(I) = ((HYDRT(I) - ANHYD(I)) /HYDRT(I))*100.$$

Of course, the subscripted variables would have to be defined in a DIMENSION statement, and some way of repeatedly executing the statement while increment-ing the subscript is needed. This is discussed in the next chapter.

CHAPTER 3

FORTRAN CONTROL

METHODS

3-1. DO LOOPS.

When the same routine is used for repeated calculations, it is obviously not convenient to write it into the program each time. In this case, being able to deviate from the linear or sequential execution of statements and return to use the same routine is preferable. Consequently, we have the loop, a series of statements repeatedly executed; the process itself is called looping. To allow the establishment of a loop in a program, it is necessary to have a statement that permits deviation from the sequential execution of statements. Such statements are called control statements. The most useful control statement, the DO statement by means of which DO loops can be established, is written

DO n $i = j_1, j_2, j_3$.

Here n is the reference number of a statement that follows the DO statement by one or more statements, i is a nonsubscripted integer variable, and the j's are nonsubscripted integer variables or positive integer constants. If j_3 is omitted, a value of 1 is assumed. The DO statement is an instruction that calls for the repeated execution of the statements following it, up to and including the statement numbered n—initially with $i = j_1$, then with $i = j_1 + j_3$ and so on, until the value of i exceeds j_2. An example of a DO statement is

DO 10 J = 1, 20

where the 10 refers to the number of the statement that is one or more statements after the DO statement. The DO statement first results in the execution of the statements up to and including statement 10, with J equal to one. The J is incremented by 1, and the statements up to and including 10 are executed again. This process is repeated as J is incremented by one ($j_3 = 1$ is implied by the absence of a j_3 value) until J exceeds 20. When J exceeds 20, the statement following statement 10 is then executed and the program continues. An example of a DO loop would be

```
    DO 2 J = 1, 999
    X = J
    ROOT = X**(.5)
    SQUARE = X**2
    CUBERT = X**(1./3.)
    CUBE = X**3
  2 PRINT 20, X, ROOT, SQUARE, CUBERT, CUBE
 20 FORMAT(1Hb, E14.7, 3XE14.7, 3XE14.7, 3XE14.7)
```

This loop is designed to tabulate the square root, square, cube root, and cube of numbers from one to 999. In the loop, J has an initial value of 1 and is incremented by 1 each time the series of statements up to and including statement 2 is executed. When J becomes 1000, the loop is not repeated, and the next executable statement following FORMAT statement 20 is executed. The sequence of statements from the DO statement to the statement numbered n comprises the DO loop and is called the range of the DO statement. If the DO loop is repeatedly executed until (and not including) the value of i exceeds the value of j_2, the DO statement is said to be satisfied and the statement following statement number n is then executed. This process is called a normal exit from the DO loop. During the execution of the DO loop, the values of i (the index) are available for use as integers within the loop. Within a DO loop, the index may be used as an integer value in the loop. For example, consider the following DO loop:

```
    DO 10 K = 1, 10
    X(K) = X(K)**Y
    Z(K) = X(K + 1)
    W(K) = 2.0*K
    N(K) = K
 10 SUM = SUM + 2.0**K
```

In this example, the values of K are used for subscripts, exponentiation, and as values for the elements of a subscripted variable. Upon normal exit from a DO loop, the value of the index is the maximum value attained.

A number of rules govern the use of DO loops.

1. The first statement of a DO loop must be an executable statement. That is, the first statement cannot be a specification statement, such as a FORMAT or DIMENSION statement.

2. The last statement in a DO loop cannot be a control statement. Often

a CONTINUE statement, which is a nonoperative statement, is used as the last statement of a DO loop to prevent the violation of this rule.

3. No statement in the DO loop can redefine the value of the index i or any of the indexing parameters, j values.

4. DO loops may be placed within DO loops. This is called the nesting of DO loops.

5. Control statements that transfer the control into DO loops are not permitted, for indexing would not be properly initiated.

6. Transfer of control from within a DO loop to a statement outside the loop is permitted; however, this is not a normal exit, so the index retains the value it had at the time transfer of control occurred.

The DO loop is a very useful method for certain types of repetitious calculations and certain input and output operations. Consider the routine to calculate the percentage by mass water in a hydrate discussed in Section 2-6. A general routine to solve this type of problem is

```
C  FORTRAN II ROUTINE
       DIMENSION PH20(20), HYDRT(20), ANHYD(20)
       READ 10, N, (HYDRT(I), ANHYD(I), I = 1, N)
   10  FORMAT(I2/(F6.4, 1XF6.4))
       SUM = 0.0
       FN = N
       DO 1 I = 1, N
       PH20(I) = ((HYDRT(I) − ANHYD(I))/HYDRT(I))*(100.)
       SUM = SUM + PH20(I)
    1  CONTINUE
       AVEPC = SUM/FN
       TYPE 20
       TYPE 30, (I, PH20(I), I = 1, N)
       TYPE 40, AVEPC
   20  FORMAT(35HPERCENTAGE BY MASS WATER IN
            HYDRATE)
   30  FORMAT(11HSAMPLE NO. I3, 5XE10.3, 2X7HPERCENT)
   40  FORMAT(21HTHE AVERAGE VALUE IS E10.3,
            1X7HPERCENT)
```

This routine is written to handle from 1 to 20 sets of data, a capacity that could be increased by increasing the maximum subscripts in the DIMENSION statement. To see how the routine functions, we can consider each statement separately.

1. The DIMENSION statement defines the subscripted variables and sets the maximum values for the subscripts.

2. The READ statement is an example of an input statement that incorpo-

rates a DO loop. Generally this is done by enclosing subscripted variables in parentheses along with the index and the indexing parameters. The READ statement is equivalent to the following statements:

```
        READ 5, N
        DO 6 I = 1, N
     6  READ 9, HYDRT(I), ANHYD(I)
```

Although writing the statement in the condensed form is allowed, it is not required, since it can be replaced by the above three statements. The READ statement in the routine, along with the FORMAT statement, results in a card containing the value of N, the number of data sets, being read; then N more cards containing values for the subscripted variables are read. As the data cards are read, the values are assigned to the variables with subscript values corresponding to the current value of I. I is incremented from 1 to N as the cards are read.

3. The FORMAT statement 10 gives the specifications of N and the values of the subscripted variables. Note that the value of N is read from one card, while the values of the subscripted variables are read two at a time from subsequent cards. Since the subscripted variable values are the same, only one set of specifications, enclosed in parentheses, is needed. However, all cards containing experimental data must meet the specification indicated.

4. Since SUM is used in the DO loop to refer to the sum of the percentages, it must be initialized as being equal to zero. This initialization of SUM is accomplished by the fourth statement.

5. The average value of the percentage is calculated by dividing the sum of the percentages by the number of values. However, since the N value is integer, its value must be assigned to a real variable so that the value may be used in expressions involving real quantities. The fifth statement provides for the conversion of the value from integer to real.

6. The sixth statement is the DO statement initiating the DO loop that accomplishes the percentage calculations and the summation of the percentages. This DO loop is executed N times, with I varying from 1 through N. Consequently, N values of PH20(I) are calculated.

7. The seventh statement is the arithmetic statement that accomplishes the percentage calculations. A different result is obtained each time this statement is executed using different subscripts.

8. The eighth statement is an arithmetic statement that sums the values of PH20(I). Each time the loop is executed, the current value of PH20(I) is added to the accumulated total.

9. The CONTINUE statement is the last statement in the DO loop and is used for convenience.

10. The tenth statement is an arithmetic statement that calculates the average percentage.

11. The eleventh statement, along with FORMAT 20, results in the output of a descriptive comment.

12. The twelfth statement, along with FORMAT 30, results in the sample number, according to the order in which the data cards were read, and the percentages being output along with descriptive commentary. Note that this output statement incorporates a DO loop in a manner analogous to the READ statement discussed above. This technique of establishing a DO loop within an output statement is a convenient way to output the accumulated values of a subscripted variable. This output statement is equivalent to and could be replaced by the following statements:

```
      DO 88 I = 1, N
   88 TYPE 30, I, PH20(I)
```

13. The last statement, along with FORMAT 40, results in the value for the average percentage being output along with descriptive commentary.

The output of this routine if three sets of data were used could be as follows-

```
PERCENTAGE BY MASS WATER IN HYDRATE
SAMPLE NO. 1        2.542E + 01 PERCENT
SAMPLE NO. 2        2.537E + 01 PERCENT
SAMPLE NO. 3        2.550E + 01 PERCENT
THE AVERAGE VALUE IS 2.543E + 01 PERCENT
```

The same routine written in FORTRAN IV is

```
C FORTRAN IV ROUTINE
      DIMENSION PH20(20), HYDRT(20), ANHYD(20)
      READ (5, 10) N, (HYDRT(I), ANHYD(I), I = 1, N)
   10 FORMAT(I2/(F6.4, 1XF6.4))
      DATA SUM/0.0/
      FN = N
      DO 1 I = 1, N
      PH20(I) = ((HYDRT(I) - ANHYD(I))/HYDRT(I))*100.
      SUM = SUM + PH20(I)
    1 CONTINUE
      AVEPC = SUM/FN
      WRITE (6, 20)
      WRITE (6, 30) (I, PH20(I), I = 1, N)
      WRITE (6, 40) AVEPC
   20 FORMAT(1H1, 35HPERCENTAGE BY MASS WATER IN
             HYDRATE)
   30 FORMAT(1Hb, 11HSAMPLE NO. I3, 5XE10.3, 2X7HPERCENT)
   40 FORMAT(1H0, 21HTHE AVERAGE VALUE IS E10.3,
             1X7HPERCENT)
```

Basically, the function of this routine is the same as the previous routine. Note the printer control characters in the output FORMAT statements.

Another routine utilizing DO loops is one designed to add two matrices of the same size. (See Section 9-1.) That is, given the two matrices X and Y with K columns and L rows each, we want a routine to find $Z = X + Y$, where each element of Z is the sum of the corresponding elements of X and Y. The routine is

```
      DO 10 I = 1, L
      DO 10 J = 1, K
   10 Z(I, J) = X(I, J) + Y(I, J)
```

Notice that this routine involves one DO loop nested within another. In such cases, the inner DO loops are completed before the outer DO loops. Trace this routine through for the simple case of two matrices with two rows and two columns each.

As another example, consider a routine designed to input a set of experimental results and then calculate the mean and standard deviation for the set. (See Section 2-3, Example 8, for the algebraic expression for the calculation of the standard deviation.) The standard deviation serves as a good measure of precision for a set of experimental results. A routine (FORTRAN II) that will read in data from cards, accomplish the calculations, and output the results is shown below.

```
      SUMX = 0.
      SUMX2 = 0.
      READ 10, N
   10 FORMAT(I3)
      DO 1 I = 1, N
      READ 20, X
   20 FORMAT(E14.7)
      SUMX = SUMX + X
      SUMX2 = SUMX2 + X**2
    1 CONTINUE
      FN = N
      FMEAN = SUMX/FN
      S = ((SUMX2 - ((SUMX**2)/FN))/(FN - 1.0))**.5
      PUNCH 30, FMEAN, S
   30 FORMAT(12HTHE MEAN IS E14.7/26HTHE STANDARD
             DEVIATION IS E14.7)
```

Let us consider the function of each statement in this routine.

1. The first two statements initialize the variables used in the summation of X and X squared.

2. The third statement results in the reading of a card that contains an integer indicating the number of data cards containing one datum each.

3. The DO statement initiates a DO loop that reads in a data card, adds the X value to SUMX, and the X squared value to SUMX2. This DO loop is executed N times and thus N cards are read in.

4. The twelfth and thirteenth statements are arithmetic statements that accomplish the calculation of the mean and standard deviation.

5. The final two statements provide for the punching of the value of the mean and standard deviation on cards, along with descriptive commentary.

3-2. IF AND GO TO STATEMENTS.

As noted earlier, statements like the DO statement that provide for deviation from the sequential execution of statements are called control statements. There are several types of control statements in the FORTRAN language. The computed IF statement allows for branching to one of three statements, depending on the algebraic nature of a variable or expression. In other words, the computed IF statement provides for the branching to a given statement based on a decision concerning the nature of a given quantity. The general form of the IF statement is

IF (exp) n_1, n_2, n_3

where exp represents a real or integer expression or variable and n_1, n_2, n_3 are statement numbers. The IF statement functions by transferring control (branching) to one of the three statements referred to by the n values, depending on the value of the parenthetical expression. The statement to which the IF statement transfers control is determined by the following considerations:

1. Branching to statement n_1 occurs if the parenthetical expression is less than zero, that is, negative.

2. Branching to statement n_2 occurs if the parenthetical expression is equal to zero.

3. Branching to statement n_3 occurs if the parenthetical expression is greater than zero, that is, positive.

A few examples of IF statements are

IF (X) 10, 20, 30

If X is negative, the program branches to statement 10; if X is zero, branching to statement 20 occurs; and if X is positive, the program branches to statement 30.

IF (A − B) 1, 2, 2

If the difference between A and B is zero or positive, branching to statement 2 occurs; otherwise branching to statement 1 occurs. Another way of stating this is that if A is greater than or equal to B, branching to statement 2 occurs, and if A is less than B, branching to statement 1 occurs. When an expression is used as the argument of an IF statement, the values of the variables must be previously defined. Of course, the variable values are not altered or destroyed by use in the argument of part of an IF statement.

IF (I − 2) 10, 20, 10

If I is equal to 2, the program branches to statement 20; otherwise the program branches to statement 10.

IF (CHECK) 112, 3, 78

If CHECK is positive, the next statement executed is 78; if CHECK is zero, then statement 3 is executed; and if CHECK is negative, statement 112 is executed.

IF ((X**2 − Y/Z + SORT*(VAL))/FACTOR) 3, 2, 1

The parenthetical expression is evaluated, and if the result is positive, branching to statement 1 occurs; if the result is zero, branching to statement 2 occurs; or, if the result is negative, branching to statement 3 occurs.

The IF statement can be used anywhere in a program except as the terminal statement of a DO loop or as the last statement in a program. The decision-making capability of the IF statement makes this control statement a very useful programming device. However, before considering some examples of routines using the IF statement, we should consider another control statement, the unconditional GO TO statement, the general form of which is GO TO *n*, where *n* is the number of an executable statement in the program. This control statement allows for direct branching to any numbered executable statement in the program. A GO TO statement can be used anywhere in a program except as the terminal statement in a DO loop or as the last statement of a program. It can be used to branch back to a previous portion of the program or to branch ahead and skip a portion of the program. The statement GO TO 5 causes the program to branch to statement number five, wherever it may be located in the program. The GO TO statement is most often used in routines involving IF statements. If we had a series of nonzero integers we wished to read from cards and classify into groups of positive and negative integers, we could accomplish this with a routine that utilizes the IF statement. Such a routine could be written in FORTRAN IV as follows:

```
      DIMENSION ID(100), IP(100), IN(100)
      READ (5, 10) N, (ID(I), I = 1, N)
   10 FORMAT(I3/(I5))
      K = 1
      L = 1
      DO 1 I = 1, N
```

```
   IF(ID(I)) 2, 3, 4
 2 IN(K) = ID(I)
   K = K + 1
   GO TO 1
 3 TYPE 30
30 FORMAT(22HERROR − A ZERO INTEGER)
   GO TO 1
 4 IP(L) = ID(I)
   L = L + 1
 1 CONTINUE
   WRITE (7, 40) (IN(I), I = 1, K)
40 FORMAT(I5)
   WRITE (7, 50) (IP(J), J = 1, L)
50 FORMAT(I5)
```

Trace through each step in this routine. Notice that the IF statement allows for branching to three different parts of the DO loop and that the GO TO statements provide for skipping portions of the loop that are unnecessary during a particular execution. In addition, note the manner in which the subscripts of the variables are established.

If we had the set of positive integers obtained from the above routine and we wanted to arrange them into sets of odd and even integers, we could use a routine involving an IF statement. To distinguish between odd and even integers, we should recall that an odd integer can be expressed as $2x + 1$, where x is an integer. Furthermore, division of an odd integer by two in integer arithmetic will always give the integer x corresponding to the original integer. A routine to separate a group of positive integers into odd and even sets would be the same as the previously described routine except that the IF statement should be replaced by

$$\text{IF (ID(I)} - ((\text{ID(I)}/2)*2 + 1)) \; 2, \, 4, \, 3$$

and statement 30 should be

```
30 FORMAT(24HERROR − NEGATIVE INTEGER)
```

Furthermore, the variable names could be changed if desired, but this is not necessary.

Occasionally, in a program, it is necessary to order a set of numbers so that they are ranked from highest to lowest. This ordering of numbers can be accomplished by a routine using an IF statement; for example,

```
NM = N − 1
DO 10 K = 1, NM
JO = K + 1
DO 10 J = JO, N
```

```
      IF(X(K) − X(J)) 5, 10, 10
   5  SAVE = X(K)
      X(K) = X(J)
      X(J) = SAVE
  10  CONTINUE
```

In this routine, N refers to the number of values of the array of numbers, X(K). After completion, the numbers will be ordered, with the highest being X(1) and the next highest being X(2), etc. Trace the routine through to see how it works, using the following set of numbers:

1, 3, 2, 4

Another IF control statement similar to the arithmetic IF statement is available in FORTRAN IV. This is the logical IF statement in which the argument of the IF statement is a logical expression rather than an arithmetic expression. The general form is

IF (log exp) *s*

In this statement, log exp represents any valid logical expression, *s* is any executable FORTRAN statement except another IF or DO statement. The function of the logical IF statement is as follows:

1. The parenthetical logical expression is evaluated.
2. If the value of the logical expression is .TRUE., statement *s* is executed. If *s* is not a control statement, the next statement following the IF statement is executed. However, if *s* is a control statement, the next statement executed is that indicated by statement *s*.
3. If the value of the logical expression is .FALSE., the statement *s* is not executed and the next statement following the IF statement is executed. An example of a logical IF statement is

IF (X − Y .LT. 1.0E−4 .OR. K .GE. 100) GO TO 10

If the difference X − Y is less than 10^{-4} or the value of K is greater than or equal to 100, the program branches to statement number 10. Keep in mind that none of the values in the logical expression is affected when the expression is evaluated. If the value of the above logical expression is .FALSE., the next statement following the IF statement is executed. To illustrate the use of the logical IF statement, consider a routine designed to read in an array of real numbers and classify them into groups of from 1 to 9, 10 to 99, and 100 to 999.

```
      DIMENSION X(100), XU(100), XT(100), XH(100)
      I = 1
  20  READ (5, 10) X(I), ID
  10  FORMAT(F3.0, 1XI2)
      IF(ID.EQ.99) GO TO 30
```

```
        I = I + 1
        GO TO 20
    30  DATA K, L, M /1, 1, 1/
        DO 80 J = 1, I
        IF (X(I) .GE. 1.00 .AND. X(I) .LT. 10.0) GO TO 50
        IF (X(I) .GE. 10.0 .AND. X(I) .LT. 100.) GO TO 60
        IF (X(I) .GE. 100. .AND. X(I) .LT. 1000.) GO TO 70
        GO TO 80
    50  XU(K) = X(I)
        K = K + 1
        GO TO 80
    60  XT(L) = X(I)
        L = L + 1
        GO TO 80
    70  XH(M) = X(I)
        M = M + 1
    80  CONTINUE
        WRITE (7, 90) (XU(I), I = 1, K), (XT(I), I = 1, L), (XH(I), I = 1, M)
    90  FORMAT(16F5.0)
```

Note that the data cards are read in by a loop controlled by a logical IF statement; only the last data card is given an ID number of 99. When the last card is read, the input is terminated. This is a convenient way to input an unknown number of cards. The number of cards read is tallied as the integer variable I. Since there will be I pieces of data, a DO loop that tests the value of $X(I)$ is set up. The DO loop includes three logical IF statements that serve to classify the data into the three possible groups. Finally, an output statement consisting of three output loops is used to output the results. The output statement results in the values of $XU(I)$ being punched, followed by the values of $XT(I)$ and then the values of $XH(I)$.

Another control statement used occasionally is the computed or conditional GO TO statement, whose general form is:

GO TO $(n_1, n_2, n_3, \ldots, n_m), i$

where the parenthetical n's comprise a list of statement numbers and i is an integer variable parameter. This statement results in the transfer of control to one of the statements in the list, depending on the value of the parameter. An example of a computed GO TO statement is

GO TO (3, 5, 5, 2, 4), I

which results in the following operations:

1. If I is one, the program branches to statement 3.
2. If I is two, the program branches to statement 5.

3. If I is three, the program branches to statement 5.
4. If I is four, the program branches to statement 2.
5. If I is five, the program branches to statement 4.

In this case, I should never exceed the value of 5. The computed GO TO statement allows for the selection of the next sequence of statements, depending on the value of the parameter I.

Computed GO TO statements are often used in general purpose programs designed to handle various situations. The value of the parameter for a given set of data can be input along with the data. The particular sequence of operations can then be selected, depending on the value of the parameter.

If we had data that were expressed in metric measure as meters, centimeters, and millimeters, and we wanted to convert the measurements to feet and inches, we could use a routine that includes computed GO TO statements and reads the parameter value from the data cards. For example, a routine to accomplish this in FORTRAN II is

```
      READ 10, N
10 FORMAT (I3)
      DO 1 I = 1, N
      READ 20, DATA, K
20 FORMAT(F6.3, 1XI1)
      GO TO (2, 3, 4), K
 2 ENG = DATA*3.937E-2
      GO TO 5
 3 ENG = DATA*3.937E-1
      IENG = ENG
      FT = IENG/12
      FIN = ENG - (FT*12.)
      GO TO 6
 4 ENG = DATA*39.37
      IENG = ENG
      FT = IENG/12
      FIN = ENG - (FT*12.)
      GO TO 7
 5 PUNCH 30, DATA, ENG
30 FORMAT(E11.4, 14HMILLIMETERS = E11.4, 7H INCHES)
      GO TO 1
 6 PUNCH 40, DATA, FT, FIN
40 FORMAT(E11.4, 14HCENTIMETERS = F3.0, 10H FEET AND
            E11.4, 7H INCHES)
      GO TO 1
 7 PUNCH 50, DATA, FT, FIN
```

```
    50 FORMAT(E11.4, 9HMETERS = F4.0, 10H FEET AND E11.4,
       7H INCHES)
     1 CONTINUE
```

This routine could process N cards, each containing a metric measurement. The value of N is read from a card that precedes the data cards. The computed GO TO statement provides for branching to the calculations that use the proper conversion factor for the metric data. Notice the technique used to convert the inches to feet and inches by means of integer arithmetic. When this technique is used, it is important to ensure that no significant digits are lost due to insufficient integer length. The metric measurement and the English equivalent are punched out for each case.

3-3. ADDITIONAL STATEMENTS.

One of the important statements in a FORTRAN program is the END statement, which must be the last source statement of the program. It indicates to the compiler that the last source statement of the program has been read, thus enabling it to begin translation of the program into machine code. The following FORTRAN statements are also available for programming.

PAUSE   This statement causes the computer to halt, and execution can only be continued by the operator of the computer. It is normally used when the programmer desires to have the operator perform some function at some point during the program, such as placing additional data cards in the card reader or setting certain switches.

STOP   This statement causes the computer to halt, and execution cannot be continued without termination of the program.

COMMON List   The COMMON statement results in the variables in the list being stored in a common storage area that makes the variables available for use in any program and accompanying subroutines.

EQUIVALENCE (list$_1$), (list$_2$), . . . , (list$_n$)   This statement results in the variables specified in a given parenthetical list being assigned the same storage locations. In this way, two or more variable names may refer to the same storage location. This statement is used to conserve storage space and allows a given area of storage to be used several times for variable values that are not being saved.

CALL EXIT   A very useful statement that causes control to be transferred from the program being executed to the monitor program, this is usually the last executable statement in a program. The END statement is the last statement, but it is not executable. The CALL EXIT statement provides for the processing of FORTRAN source programs in batches. When the CALL EXIT shifts control to the monitor, the next source program in the card reader is read in and compiled. This is time saving and enables the operator to stack batches of programs in the card reader or to run batches of programs from some other input medium. A program should have an END statement, and a CALL EXIT statement should be used when monitor control is being utilized. The following routine for density calculations would be considered to be a program, for it contains an END statement.

```
      DIMENSION XMASS(50), VOL(50), DEN(50), TEMP(50)
      READ 10, N, (XMASS(I), VOL(I), TEMP(I), I = 1, N)
   10 FORMAT(I3/(E14.7, 1XE14.7, 1XF4.1))
      DO 30 I = 1, N
   30 DEN(I) = XMASS(I)/VOL(I)
      PRINT 20, (I, DEN(I), TEMP(I), I = 1, N)
   20 FORMAT(1Hb, 12HDENSITY NO. I4, 3H = E14.7, 1X12HAT
             TEMP. OF F5.0, 1X9HDEGREES C)
      CALL EXIT
      END
```

When programs are written in this manner and the compiler is under monitor control, many programs can be compiled and executed consecutively without the intervention of the computer operator. However, this statement should not be used unless the compiler is controlled by a monitor program. Some monitored systems use a statement other than CALL EXIT to transfer control back to the monitor.

3-4. VARIABLE FORMAT STATEMENTS.

Sometimes it is advisable to vary the input and output FORMAT statements in a program in order to fit the data that are to be used. This process usually requires rewriting the FORMAT statements. FORTRAN IV allows for the input of FORMAT statements in the form of data that can be input as variable values using A specification. This input is facilitated by allowing the use of variable names in place of statement numbers in input and output statements. For example, instead of writing

READ (5, 10) list

the statement

READ (5, FRMT) list

can be used. FRMT is the name of a variable that contains the previously input FORMAT specifications. Because most FORMAT statements are several characters long and they must be input as alphabetic variables, it is necessary to input them in parts as elements of a subscripted variable. Furthermore, only the parenthetical portion of the FORMAT statement needs to be input, since the keyword FORMAT is implied by the context. An example of the statements needed to accomplish the input of FORMAT statements and the use of the statements is given below.

```
      DIMENSION FIN(12), FOUT(12)
      READ (5, 10) (FIN(I), I = 1, 12), (FOUT(I), I = 1, 12)
   10 FORMAT(12A6)
      –

      READ (5, FIN) X, Y, Z
      –

      WRITE (6, FOUT) X, Y, Z, ANSWER
      –
```

The DIMENSION statement defines the variables FIN and FOUT as subscripted variables. The first READ statement sets up an input loop to input data cards containing the FORMAT statements to be used in the program. FORMAT statement number 10 specifies these data cards as consisting of 12 blocks of 6 alphameric characters each. This results in a total of 72 characters being read for variable FIN and 72 characters being read for variable FOUT. Such FORMAT data cards could be

(F6.3, 1XF8.5, 5XE14.8)

and (1Hb, F6.3, 5XF8.5, 5XE14.8, / 14HTHE ANSWER IS E14.8)

The second READ statement refers to the variable FIN, which is the previously read FORMAT statement in the form of a subscripted variable. Only the name FIN is needed to refer to all the elements of FIN(I). This READ statement results in the values of X, Y, and Z being read according to the specifications given by FIN. The WRITE statement uses the previously read output FORMAT, which is stored as the subscripted variable FOUT(I) to output the variables X, Y, Z, and ANSWER. The name FOUT refers to the complete subscripted variable FOUT(I).

This technique of using variable FORMAT specifications is convenient with programs that are general and where the form of the data is not known at the time the program is written. As a rule, the form of the data is known or can be expressed in E form, so the more complex procedure of providing for the input of the FORMAT statements need not be included in most programs.

CHAPTER 4

FORTRAN SUBPROGRAM

TECHNIQUES

4-1. LIBRARY SUBROUTINES.

When writing a FORTRAN program, we often have occasion to use a routine that involves a general type of calculation. For example, to find the square root of a number, we could devise a square root routine and use it in the program when desired. Routines repeatedly used in the program are called subroutines or subprograms. Several common mathematical operations have been written as subroutines and are incorporated into the compiler for availability to the programmer. These subroutines are called library subroutines and can be called into a program by using certain keywords. For example, the statement ROOT = SQRTF(X), which contains the keyword SQRTF, indicates to the compiler that the square root subroutine is to be used to calculate the square root of X and the result is to be assigned to the variable name ROOT. Some typical library subroutines and their functions are listed in Table 4-1.

Some compilers use other keywords. Furthermore, many computer installations have several additional library subroutines available for FORTRAN programmers. Information concerning the availability of other library subroutines and the keywords used for all library routines can be obtained from the computer center or the computer specifications manual.

When the keyword indicating a subroutine appears in an expression, it serves essentially to call for the use of the subroutine that is part of the compiler library. Every time a subroutine is called, the argument to be used with the subroutine must be enclosed in the parentheses following the keyword. This argument can be a real constant, variable, or expression. Furthermore, the

TABLE 4-1. Typical Library Subroutines

Name	Keyword FORTRAN II	FORTRAN IV	Example	Function
Square root	SQRTF	SQRT	X = SQRTF(Y) X = SQRT(Y)	The square root of Y is assigned to X.
Sine	SINF	SIN	X = SINF(Y) X = SIN(Y)	The sine of Y (units of radians) assigned as value of X.
Cosine	COSF	COS	X = COSF(Y) X = COS(Y)	The cosine of Y (units of radians) is assigned as value of X.
Arctangent	ATANF	ATAN	X = ATANF(Y) X = ATAN(Y)	The arctangent of Y or angle which has a tangent Y is assigned as value of X.
Absolute value	ABSF	ABS	X = ABSF(Y) X = ABS(Y)	The absolute value of Y is assigned as value of X.
Exponential (antilog)	EXPF	EXP	X = EXPF(Y) X = EXP(Y)	The value of e^Y is assigned as value of X.
Logarithm	LOGF	ALOG	X = LOGF(Y) X = ALOG(Y)	The value of ln Y (base e) is assigned as value of X.
		ALOG10	X = ALOG10(Y)	The value of log y (base 10) is assigned as value of X.

keyword with the desired argument can be utilized as part of a complex arithmetic statement. Some examples of arithmetic statements using library subroutines are

FORTRAN IV

$$S = SQRT(((SUMX2) - (SXDN2))/(FN - 1.0))$$
$$X = ((-B + SQRT(B**2 - 4.*A*C))/(2.*A))$$
$$ROOT = SQRT(SQRT(ABS(X)))$$

FORTRAN II

$$S = SQRTF(((SUMX2) - (SXDN2))/(FN - 1.0))$$
$$X = ((-B + SQRTF(B**2 - 4.*A*C))/(2.*A))$$
$$ROOT = SQRTF(SQRTF(ABSF(X)))$$

Notice that these statements involve the use of subroutines within arguments. In these cases, the innermost argument is determined using the indicated subroutines and so on, until the outermost subroutine is used. Generally any subroutine may be used in the argument of another subroutine.

FORTRAN IV

SINE = SIN(FACTOR*45.)
RESULT = (5.30*COS(ANGLE))/8.37
ANGLE = 57.296*ATAN(X)
PH = (ALOG10(1.0/H))
E = EO − ((.059/FN)*ALOG10(RED/OX))

FORTRAN II

SINE = SINF(FACTOR*45.)
RESULT = (5.30*COSF(ANGLE))/8.37
ANGLE = 57.296*ATANF(X)
PH = (LOGF(1.0/H))/2.303
E = EO − ((.059/FN)*(LOGF(RED/OX)/2.303))

4-2. ARITHMETIC STATEMENT FUNCTION.

Library subroutines are available for calculations used repeatedly. Often, in a complex program, a certain type of calculation or a series of calculations is carried out repeatedly with different data. Then it would be convenient to state the general calculations once and use them as often as necessary throughout the program. When the calculations involve only one statement, this statement can be written once and used repeatedly if it is written in the form of an arithmetic statement function. The arithmetic statement function provides a way to assign a keyword to a general arithmetic statement so that the keyword can be used to refer to the statement. That is, the programmer is able to set up a function that can be used in a manner analogous to the library subroutines. The general form for the definition of an arithmetic statement function is

NAME(variable list) = arithmetic expression using variables in list

The NAME is the keyword that the programmer desires to use to refer to the function. Formation of this name follows the normal rules for variable names except that some compilers require that the name end in the letter F. The variable list refers to a list of nonsubscripted variables corresponding in order and mode to the variables used in the expression written to the right of the equal sign. When a statement function is first defined, these variable names serve as dummy variables. That is, they are variables with no established values but only serve to indicate the positions in the expression where real variables are to be used. The function is called into use in the program by stating the keyword name, followed by the actual variables to be used enclosed in parentheses. For example, the statement ANS = NAMEF(X) results in the value of the variable X being used in the previously defined arithmetic statement function called NAMEF, with the results then being assigned as the value of ANS. The statement defining the function must precede any executable statement in the program. An arithmetic statement function and a statement using it would be

FUNCF(X) = X**(1./3.)
CUBRT = FUNCF(Y)

The first statement defines the function called FUNCF as a function of the dummy variable X, which is to determine the cube root of the variable. Of course, the X merely serves to indicate the mode and position of the variable, and the defining statement alone does not result in any calculations. The second statement shown is an example of a statement in the program that calls the function into use via the keyword FUNCF, followed by the actual argument Y in parentheses. This statement results in the value of Y being used as the argument in the arithmetic statement function, and the result of the calculation is assigned as the value of CUBRT. Once the function is defined, it can be used in any expression in the program any number of times. Another statement using the above function could be

RESULT = (Z/3.0E2) − FUNCF(DATA*FACTOR)

In this statement, the value for the argument is first evaluated, then used as the argument of the function, and the result subtracted from the value of Z/3.0E2. The final value is then assigned as the value of RESULT. Whenever a calculation is used often in a program, an arithmetic statement function can be employed to avoid rewriting the expression each time it is needed.

Functions may be defined using more than one variable, and the variables can be real or integer. For example, the function

POLYF(X, I1, I2, Y) = X**I1 + X**I2 + X*Y

includes two real and two integer dummy variables. The dummy variables enclosed in parentheses must correspond in order and mode to the variables in the expression. When the function is called into use, each actual variable must be specified and must have a value. The above function could be called by a statement like the following:

EQU = POLYF(VAR(I), N, 2, A)

which is equivalent to writing the statement

EQU = VAR(I)**N + VAR(I)**2 + VAR(I)*A

Of course, when execution occurs, values for VAR(I), N, and A must have been previously established. Since VAR(I) refers to an array, it must have been previously dimensioned and the value of I must be established before VAR(I) can be used in the function. Also, note that one of the actual arguments used in the above expression is a constant. This is permitted.

Arithmetic statement functions can serve to simplify the writing of a program. If we wanted to use base ten logarithms, we could set up the function

LOGTF(ARG) = LOGF(ARG)/LOGF(10.)

and then use the keyword LOGTF, followed by the argument when needed. If we wanted to find the cosines of angles expressed in degrees, we could set up the function

COSDF(X) = COSF(X/57.2958)

Then the keyword COSDF could be used in any statement to call the function into use.

4-3. FUNCTION AND SUBROUTINE SUBPROGRAMS.

Although the arithmetic statement function is convenient, it can only be used for calculations involving one statement. Frequently, repetitive calculations that involve a series of arithmetic and control statements are carried out. Consequently, it is desirable to be able to establish a subroutine or subprogram that can be branched to from the main program when the subprogram is needed. FORTRAN provides two methods of establishing subprograms, the FUNCTION subprogram and the SUBROUTINE subprogram. The advantages of subprograms are that they can be compiled independently of the main program, and if generally written, they can be used with any main program. Any group of statements used frequently can be written in the form of a subprogram. Furthermore, a large program may be split into parts that can be written as subprograms and worked upon separately. After the subprograms have been worked out, they can be linked together to form the complete program. The general form of the FUNCTION subprogram is

        FUNCTION NAME (dummy variable list)
        . . .
        . . .
        NAME = expression
        . . .
        . . .
        RETURN
        END

The first statement, which contains the keyword FUNCTION, followed by the name and the parenthetical dummy variables, serves to define the subsequent statements as a subprogram referred to as NAME. The formation of the name of the subprogram follows the normal rules for naming variables; but, with some compilers, the name must end in the letter F. The list of dummy variables must correspond in terms of mode, number, and order to the way in which the variables are used in subsequent statements of the subprogram. As many variables and statements as desired may be used in the subprogram. However, the name of the subprogram must appear to the left of an equal sign in an arithmetic statement within the subprogram. The value assigned to the name when the subprogram is executed is normally considered to be the result calculated by the subroutine. If any of the dummy variables are to be subscripted in the subprogram, the variable must be defined in a DIMENSION statement within the subprogram. Furthermore, the corresponding real variable in the main program must also be defined with similar dimensions. As an example of a FUNCTION subprogram, consider a routine to find the mean of an array of numbers. This routine can be written in the form of a subprogram.

```
C  AN EXAMPLE OF A FUNCTION SUBPROGRAM
         FUNCTION XBARF(A, N)
         DIMENSION A(200)
         SUM = 0.0
         FN = N
         DO 1 I = 1, N
       1 SUM = SUM + A(I)
         XBARF = SUM/FN
         RETURN
         END
```

The dummy variable A is a subscripted variable in the subprogram; thus it must be dimensioned in the subprogram. However, it must not appear in the subscripted form in the parentheses of the FUNCTION statement; this is not allowed. The real variable array to be used in the subprogram must be dimensioned in a similar manner. Notice that in the above subprogram the name of the subprogram, XBARF, is used in the seventh statement, which establishes the value of the mean.

Since the result of the subprogram is usually the value associated with the arithmetic statement containing the name of the subprogram on the left of the equal sign, the subprogram should be designed to satisfy this requirement. The subprogram must contain a RETURN statement as the final statement to be executed. The RETURN statement provides for the branching back to the main program after the subprogram has been used. More than one RETURN statement may be used in a FUNCTION subprogram if needed; for example, when more than one path of execution is incorporated in the subprogram. In the subprogram given above, the RETURN statement appears as the last executable statement. This statement results in transferring control back to the main program. A RETURN statement may be used anywhere in the subprogram and in as many positions as needed. The END statement is physically the last source statement in the subprogram. The END statement allows for the compilation of the subprogram independently of the main program.

The FUNCTION subprogram is called into use by the main program by using the name of the subprogram in an expression, followed by the actual arguments in parentheses. This is analogous to the use of the arithmetic statement function in a program. The name of the subprogram in an expression results in the actual arguments being used in the subprogram to obtain the desired results, which are then used in the expression. The subprogram given above could be called into use by the statement

FMEAN = XBARF(X, N)

which would result in the determination of the mean of N numbers of an array called X(I) and the assignment of the value of mean to the variable name FMEAN. Even though the complete array X(I) is used in the subprogram, the subscripted form is not used as an argument of the subprogram but, rather, the unsubscripted form, X. Of course, the array X(I) must be dimensioned and have previously established values, and the value of N must correspond to the number of X(I) values. Once a subroutine has been written, it can be used in any expression within the main program any number of times. For example, XBARF could appear in statements such as

AVE = (XBARF(DATA, J) + XBARF(ARRAY, NUM))/2.0

or

RESULT = SQRTF(XBARF(X,L))

or

ANS = XBARF(XNUM, NUMBER) + STNDEV

The FUNCTION subprogram is convenient when writing general routines designed to produce one result each time they are used. To illustrate another FUNCTION subprogram, consider a program showing the distribution of solute during a countercurrent extraction process. The countercurrent extraction method is a process that efficiently isolates a solute by repeated liquid-liquid extractions. The method is used for the separation and purification of the solutes in a solution. Since a liquid-liquid extraction process is involved in the method, two immiscible solvents in which the solutes are soluble are employed. The countercurrent extraction method utilizes two sets of specially designed containers. For purposes of discussion, one set can contain equal volumes of liquid O and the other set equal volumes of liquid W. These liquid phases can be referred to as $O_0, O_1, O_2, \cdots, O_i$ and $W_0, W_1, W_2, \cdots, W_i$. The solute to be extracted is in solution in phase W_0. In the first step in the extraction, phase O_0 and W_0 are mixed. After the solute has equilibrated between phases, the O_0 phase is then mixed with the W_1 phase, and the O_1 phase is mixed with the W_0 phase. The transfer process is repeated n times; each time the O phases are mixed with the next higher W phase, and a new O phase is introduced. The procedure can be illustrated as follows.

In the first step, phases W_0 and O_0 are placed in contact:

$$O_i \cdots O_3\, O_2\, O_1\, O_0$$
$$W_0\, W_1\, W_2\, W_3 \cdots W_i$$

The first extraction gives

$$O_i \cdots O_3\, O_2\, O_1\, O_0$$
$$W_0\, W_1\, W_2\, W_3 \cdots W_i$$

The second extraction gives

$$O_i \cdots O_3\, O_2\, O_1\, O_0$$
$$W_0\, W_1\, W_2\, W_3 \cdots W_i$$

The process can be repeated n times.

As the countercurrent extraction process is carried out, the solute will become dispersed in all phases. However, in most cases, the solute will be of highest concentration in the central phases. Of course, the distribution of the solute depends on the relative solubilities in the solvents. The relative solubilities are expressed in terms of the partition coefficient D. The partition coefficient for solute x in solvents W and O is defined as

$$D = \frac{\text{Concentration of } x \text{ in } O}{\text{Concentration of } x \text{ in } W} = \frac{[x_O]}{[x_W]}.$$

The fractions of the solute in the containers after n extractions are given by the terms of the binomial expansion

$$\left(\frac{1}{1+D} + \frac{D}{1+D} \right)^n.$$

Each term can be expressed as the fraction f of the solute in container i after n extractions and can be calculated by

$$f_{i,n} = \frac{(n!)(D^i)}{i!(n-i)!(1+D)^n}.$$

The $n!$ and other terms followed by ! refer to the factorials of these terms. The factorial of a number is given by the expression

$$n! = (n)(n-1)(n-2) \cdots (1).$$

In order to calculate the fractions of solute in each container after n extractions, a program utilizing a FUNCTION subprogram to find factorials of numbers can be written. For example, a program in FORTRAN II would be

```
C THIS IS THE SUBPROGRAM TO FIND FACTORIALS
      FUNCTION FACTNF(NUM)
      IF(NUM) 1, 2, 3
    1 FACTNF = 0.0
      RETURN
```

```
  2 FACTNF = 1.0
    RETURN
  3 FACTNF = 1.0
    DO 4 I = 1, NUM
    F = I
  4 FACTNF = FACTNF*F
    RETURN
    END
```

```
C THIS IS THE MAIN PROGRAM WHICH CALCULATES THE
          FRACTIONS
    READ 10, N, D
 10 FORMAT(I4, 2XF6.3)
    TYPE 20, D, N
 20 FORMAT(50HTHE DISTRIBUTION OF A SOLUTE WITH
          PARTITION COEFF F7.3,/
   18 HAFTER I4, 15H EXTRACTIONS IS)
    CONST = FACTNF(N)/(1. + D)**N
    DO 30 I = 1, N
    FIN = (CONST*D**I) / FACTNF(I) / FACTNF(N - I)
 30 TYPE 40, I, FIN
 40 FORMAT(9HCONTAINER I4, 5XE14.7)
    CALL EXIT
    END
```

This program results in a data card being read for the values of *N*, the number of extractions, and for *D*, the partition coefficient. Then the fraction of the solute in each container is calculated and recorded. Typical input and output are shown in Table 4-2. The subprogram can be compiled separately, but it must be available for use with the main program. The technique used to link the subprogram to the main program is discussed in Appendix 3. Of course, the factorial calculations could be written as part of the main program, but the subprogram is written in a general form and could be used with any program to find the factorials of numbers.

The SUBROUTINE subprogram is similar to the FUNCTION subprogram, but it is more useful. The SUBROUTINE subprogram supplies one or more results to the main program, and no value is associated with the subroutine name. The general form is

```
    SUBROUTINE NAME (dummy variable list)
    . . .
    . . .
    RETURN
    END
```

TABLE 4-2. Input and Output for the Counter Current Extraction Program

Input	0025	01.000
Output		

THE DISTRIBUTION OF SOLUTE WITH PARTITION COEFF 1.000
AFTER 25 EXTRACTIONS IS

CONTAINER	1	$7.4505803E-07$
CONTAINER	2	$8.9406963E-06$
CONTAINER	3	$6.8545336E-05$
CONTAINER	4	$3.7699933E-04$
CONTAINER	5	$1.5833972E-03$
CONTAINER	6	$5.2779907E-03$
CONTAINER	7	$1.4325974E-02$
CONTAINER	8	$3.2233439E-02$
CONTAINER	9	$6.0885384E-02$
CONTAINER	10	$9.7416612E-02$
CONTAINER	11	$1.3284083E-01$
CONTAINER	12	$1.5498097E-01$
CONTAINER	13	$1.5498097E-01$
CONTAINER	14	$1.3284083E-01$
CONTAINER	15	$9.7416617E-02$
CONTAINER	16	$6.0885386E-02$
CONTAINER	17	$3.2233439E-02$
CONTAINER	18	$1.4325974E-02$
CONTAINER	19	$5.2779906E-03$
CONTAINER	20	$1.5833971E-03$
CONTAINER	21	$3.7699934E-04$
CONTAINER	22	$6.8545336E-05$
CONTAINER	23	$8.9406960E-06$
CONTAINER	24	$7.4505803E-07$
CONTAINER	25	$2.9802322E-08$

The first statement containing the keyword SUBROUTINE serves to define the subsequent statements as a subprogram referred to as NAME. The NAME consists of from one to six alphabetic or numeric characters, the first of which must be alphabetic. The list of dummy variables gives the number, mode, and order of variables that are to be used by the subroutine or that are to have values calculated by the subroutine. This is an important difference between the two types of subprograms; that is, the SUBROUTINE list of dummy variables contains any number of arguments to be used in the subprogram and any number of variables that correspond to the results of the calculations. Some variables may be real and some may be integer, depending on the nature of the subprogram. Following is an example of the defining statement of a SUBROUTINE:

SUBROUTINE RTROUT(X, Y, N, ANS, J)

In this statement, the X, Y, and N could correspond to the variables used from the main program and the ANS and J could correspond to the variables that are to have values established by the subroutine.

The SUBROUTINE subprogram must have one or more RETURN statements to transfer control back to the main program after the subprogram has been used. The END statement must be physically the last source statement of the subprogram so that the subprogram can be compiled independently of the main program. The SUBROUTINE subprogram is called into use by the main program with a CALL statement, which has the general form:

CALL NAME (actual variable list)

The keyword CALL results in the use of the actual arguments listed in the subroutine given by the NAME. The list variables must correspond in number, order, mode, and array dimensions to the list of dummy variables in the subroutine. Any subscripted variable argument must be referred to in the unsubscripted form when it is used in the argument-variable list. The SUBROUTINE referred to above could be called into use by a main program with the statement

CALL RTROUT(DATA, A, NUM, RESULT, N)

This CALL statement, which must consist of a single source statement, results in the values of DATA, A, and NUM being used in the subprogram RTROUT to produce values for RESULT and N. This would serve to establish values for RESULT and N that could be used in further calculations or output by the main program.

The SUBROUTINE subprogram is the most useful and flexible of the two subprogramming methods. A subroutine can be compiled and used with any main program as long as the CALL statement contains the correctly listed variables and the dimensions of the subscripted variables in the subprogram and the main program are the same. Whenever a series of calculations in a program can be generalized, it is often convenient to write the calculations in the form of a SUBROUTINE. For a complex program, it is usually easier to separate the program so that it can be written as a series of SUBROUTINES to be used with one main program. As an example of the use of a SUBROUTINE subprogram with a main program, consider a program to calculate empirical formulas for compounds from percentage by mass composition data. The calculations involve determination of the number of moles of each element and the molar ratios. However, to find the molar ratios, it is necessary to divide the number of moles of each element by the smallest number of moles. To do this, the smallest number of moles must be determined by ordering the molar values. This could be done with an ordering SUBROUTINE (see Section 3-2). Furthermore, it is necessary to input the percentages, number of grams per mole for each element, and the symbol for each element. If we order the molar values for the elements, we must note which element changes place by ordering the element symbols at the same time. However, we cannot do this by using H specifications for the symbols. If we want to manipulate alphabetic data in a program, we must use A specification.

The following FORTRAN II program, with accompanying SUBROUTINE, is designed to read cards containing percentage composition, grams per mole, and element symbol data and then determine the molar ratios from which the empirical formula can be deduced.

```
C THIS IS A SUBROUTINE TO ORDER THE ELEMENTS OF ARRAY
       X(I)
C ACCORDING TO SIZE AND TO ORDER THE ELEMENTS OF
       ARRAY Y(I)
C ACCORDING TO THE REARRANGEMENT OF ARRAY X(I)
C
       SUBROUTINE ORD(N, X, Y)
       DIMENSION X(20), Y(20)
       NM = N − 1
       DO 10 K = 1, NM
       JO = K + 1
       DO 10 J = JO, N
       IF(X(K) − X(J)) 5, 10, 10
     5 SAVE = X(K)
       SAV = Y(K)
       X(K) = X(J)
       Y(K) = Y(J)
       X(J) = SAVE
       Y(J) = SAV
    10 CONTINUE
       RETURN
       END


C PROGRAM TO DETERMINE EMPIRICAL FORMULAS FROM
       PERCENTAGE
C BY MASS DATA
C
       DIMENSION (P20), GPM(20), EL(20), FMOLES(20)
       READ 10, N, (P(I), GPM(I), EL(I), I = 1, N)
    10 FORMAT(I3/(F6.3, 2XF7.3, 2XA2)) ·
       DO 1 I = 1, N
     1 FMOLES(I) = (P(I)*100.)/GPM(I)
       CALL ORD(N, FMOLES, EL)
       DO 2 I = 1, N
     2 FMOLES(I) = FMOLES(I)/FMOLES(N)
       TYPE 20, (EL(I), FMOLES(I), I = 1, N)
```

```
20 FORMAT(A2, 2XE14.7)
   CALL EXIT
   END
```

Typical input data cards and output results are shown below.
Data card form according to FORMAT 10

003		This card gives N, the number of elements.
47.000	012.010 C	This is the data card for carbon.
09.900	001.008 H	This is the data card for hydrogen.
27.400	014.010 N	This is the data card for nitrogen.

The output for this data according to FORMAT 20 would be

```
H   5.0218328E−00
C   2.0009785E−00
N   1.0000000E−00
```

From this output we could deduce an empirical formula of C_2H_5N. Of course, all eight digits in the output results are not significant digits.

Prewritten subroutines are available for a variety of numerical calculations, and most computer installations have a library of such subroutines. It is convenient to use a prewritten subroutine for a fairly complex numerical calculation; however, for common and relatively elementary numerical calculations it is instructive to write your own subroutines for use with your programs. The technique of using subroutines with programs on the computer is discussed in Appendix 3.

Problems for Part One

1. Make a list of the statements and concepts that are applicable to FORTRAN IV but not applicable to FORTRAN II.

2. Convert all FORTRAN II routines in Chapter 2 to FORTRAN IV and vice versa.

3. Explain the function of each of the following statements:
   (a) C   THIS IS A COMMENT
   (b) X = Y
   (c) X = J
   (d) X = 2.0
   (e) IF (X) 1, 1, 2
   (f) IF (X − Y) 1, 2, 3
   (g) GO TO 12
   (h) GO TO (9, 9, 2, 3, 5), J
   (i) DO 10 I = 1, 10

(j) IF(X.GT. T.OR. X.LT. Z) FUNC = 0.0
(k) DATA X, Y, Z /2.0, 1.0E5, 10.72/
(l) DIMENSION X(10, 10), Y(10), N(3, 4, 5)
(m) PRINT 20, ((X(I, J), I = 1, 5), J = 1, 10)
(n) READ 2, N, (ARRAY(I), I = 1, N)
(o) WRITE (7, 10)(X(I), I = 1, N), (Y(I), I = 1, N)
(p) TYPE 10, A(1), A(2), B, X, N, J

4. Write some FORMAT statements that could be used with the statements given in (m), (n), (o), and (p) of Problem 2.

5. What is wrong with each of the following statements?
(a) X*Y = A
(b) GO TO J
(c) N = ((Y**2)*X**3)**(1/2)
(d) N = J**.5
(e) X = X* − ANSWERS
(f) IF (X. NOT. Y) GO TO 10
(g) IF (X. GT. Y. LT. Z) DO 10 I = 1, 5

6. Write an arithmetic statement function that could be used for each of the following functions:
(a) $y = x^n$
(b) $\sin (2x) = 2 \sin (x) \cos (x)$
(c) $\log_a (x) = \log_e (x)/\log_e (a)$
(d) $y = ax^4 + bx^3 + cx^2 + dx + e$
(e) $y = 2x^2 + \ln x - |x|^{1/2} + \sin x$
(f) $y = 3x + 5z + 7w$

Bibliography for Part One

IBM 7040/7044 Operating Systems FORTRAN IV Language, Form No. C28-6329-3, IBM Corp. (1965)

IBM 7090/7094 Programming Systems FORTRAN IV Language, Form No. C28-6274-3, IBM Corp. (1964)

IBM 7090 FORTRAN II Programming, Form No. C28-6054-5, IBM Corp.

IBM System/360 FORTRAN Language, Form No. C28-6515-1, IBM Corp.

FORTRAN IV Language Specifications, IBM 1401, 1400, and 1460, Form No. C24-3322-0, IBM Corp.

IBM 1620 FORTRAN II Programming System Reference Manual, Form No. C26-5876-2, IBM Corp.

CDC 3200 Computer System FORTRAN Reference Manual, Pub No. 60057600, Control Data Corp. (1964)

UNIVAC III FORTRAN, Form No. U-3517, Sperry Rand Corp.

SDS FORTRAN II Reference Manual, Form No. SDS 900003C, Scientific Data Corp.

SDS FORTRAN IV Reference Manual, Form No. SDS 900500A, Scientific Data Corp.

Harris, L. Dale, *FORTRAN Programming (II and IV)*, Charles E. Merrill Books, Columbus, Ohio (1964)

Golde, H., *FORTRAN II and IV for Engineers and Scientists*, The Macmillan Company, New York (1966)

McCraken, D. D., *A Guide to FORTRAN Programming*, John Wiley and Sons, New York (1961)

McCraken, D. D., *A Guide to FORTRAN IV Programming*, John Wiley and Sons, New York (1965)

PART II

NUMERICAL METHODS AND COMPUTER APPLICATIONS

CHAPTER 5

PROGRAM WRITING

5-1. CODING TECHNIQUES.

The purpose of this chapter is to discuss the procedures involved in writing and preparing a FORTRAN program for use on the computer. Three example programs, as well as detailed descriptions and programming suggestions, are presented. A FORTRAN program may be written to accomplish a general calculation process or to solve a very specific problem. In any case, the approach to the preparation and use of the program can be generalized as shown in the following steps.

1. Obtain a complete statement of the problem, including the theoretical aspects needed for an unambiguous interpretation of it.

2. Plan an approach to the solution of the problem. Systematize the approach in the form of a flow chart. (See Section 1-3 for a discussion of flow charting.)

3. Write the FORTRAN statements needed to accomplish the steps involved in the flow-charted solution. This, of course, constitutes the FORTRAN program. Use a FORTRAN coding form if available and try to avoid erroneous use of the language. Follow the logic of the FORTRAN program by mentally checking the steps involved. Check also for incorrectly formed FORTRAN statements. The checking process is very important and can avoid wasting personal and computer time.

4. Prepare a FORTRAN source program by punching each statement on a card. (If card-punching service is available, submit the prepared program for punching.) In addition, punch any data cards that are to be used with the program. Be sure that the form of the data cards corresponds precisely to the FORMAT statements used in the program. Checking to see that the cards are punched properly is important.

5. Submit the source program and data cards for processing. Include a

brief description of the processing job and an identification of the program. Most computer installations have standard forms to be filled out by the programmer when requesting a processing job. If you are operating the computer yourself, follow the operation procedure for the processing of a FORTRAN program.

Once your program has been processed, you will obtain the results of the processing. In most cases, these results will be the answers and descriptive information that your program was designed to output. However, if some difficulty arose in the processing of your program, you will receive a description of the difficulty. The difficulties may be listed in the form of numerical codes used by the compiler (see Appendix 1), or they may be briefly described by the computer operator. If your program did not function correctly, you should find the errors and correct them; this is called debugging the program. Once your program has been debugged, it can be submitted for reprocessing. To increase the chance of successful processing, the program should be thoroughly scrutinized before submission. The checking process is vital and should not be neglected.

The best way to illustrate programming techniques and methods of handling various types of data is to give several examples of program preparation. When reading the examples, notice the methods used for input, output, the manipulation of data, and the manner in which the calculation loops are designed.

EXAMPLE 1

1. Write a program to illustrate the relationship between the pH of an aqueous solution of a strong acid and the acid-base properties of water. This can be shown by calculating the pH values of increasingly dilute solutions of the acid. For a solution of hydrochloric acid, the hydronium ion concentration is determined from the following considerations:

Charge balance $\qquad$ $[H_3O^+] = [Cl^-] + [OH^-]$
Ion product of water $\qquad$ $K_w = [OH^-][H_3O^+]$.

These relationships can be used to establish a quadratic equation in terms of $[H_3O^+]$:

$$[H_3O^+] = [Cl^-] + \frac{K_w}{[H_3O^+]}$$

or

$$[H_3O^+]^2 - [Cl^-][H_3O^+] - K_w = 0.$$

The $[Cl^-]$ is equal to the molarity of the acid and K_w is a known constant. The $[H_3O^+]$ can be determined using the quadratic algorithm (see Section 7-1). Since b is negative, the form of the algorithm to be used is

$$x = \frac{-b + (b^2 - 4ac)^{1/2}}{2a}.$$

To illustrate the change in pH with concentration of the acid, the concentration can be varied in tenfold increments from 1 *M* to the molarity at which the pH is constant to eight digits. Actually, the pH will continuously change as the concentration changes and will approach 7 as the concentration decreases. However, the principle can be seen by calculating the pH to eight digits. Of course, extremely dilute solutions of acids are not meant to represent real solutions, but are used only to demonstrate the fact that no matter now dilute the solution of the acid becomes, the pH will never exceed 7.

2. A flow chart for the program to solve the preceding problem appears in Figure 5-1.

3. A FORTRAN II program written from the flow chart is

```
C PROGRAM TO CALCULATE THE PH OF HCL SOLUTIONS
C
C ARITHMETIC FUNCTION TO FIND HYDRONIUM ION CONCEN-
        TRATION
      HFUNF(A) = (A + (A**2 + 4.*FKW)**.5)/2.0
C INITIALIZATION OF VARIABLES
      CA = 1.0
      PHS = 0.9
      FKW = 1.0E-14
C OUTPUT OF DESCRIPTION AND HEADINGS
      TYPE 10
   10 FORMAT(14HPH OF HCL SOLU / 2HCA 20X1HH 20X2HPH)
C CALCULATION LOOP
    5 H = HFUNF(CA)
      PH = -LOGF(H)/2.303
C OUTPUT OF CALCULATED RESULTS
      TYPE 20, CA, H, PH
   20 FORMAT(E14.7, 6XE14.7, 6XE14.7)
C COMPARISON OF CURRENT AND FORMER PH
      IF(ABSF(PHS - PH) - 1.0E-8) 2, 2, 1
C SAVE CURRENT PH
    1 PHS = PH
C DECREMENT THE ACID CONCENTRATION
      CA = CA/10.0
C BRANCH BACK TO START OF CALCULATION LOOP
      GO TO 5
C INDICATE THE END OF CALCULATIONS
    2 TYPE 30
   30 FORMAT(22HEND OF PH CALCULATIONS)
      CALL EXIT
      END
```

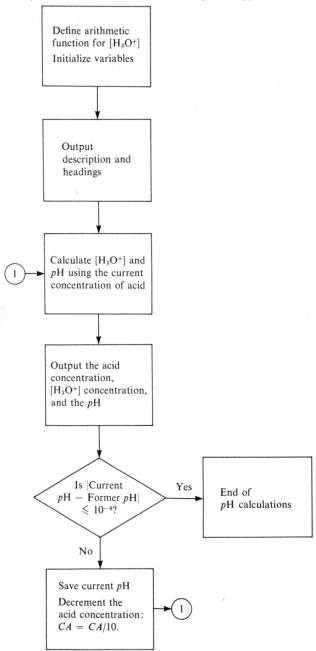

FIG. 5-1. Flow chart for the calculation of the pH for various concentrations of strong acid.

The numerous comment statements used in the preceding program are for clarification purposes; normally it would not be necessary to use so many. The first step in the program is to set up an arithmetic function statement to define the calculation of the hydronium ion concentration. Note that the algorithm has been changed to account for the negative signs of b and c. It is not necessary to use an arithmetic function statement in this case, but it is convenient. Next, a program description is output, along with some headings to describe the tabular output that is to follow. In the next few statements, the variables are defined and initialized. The initial acid concentration (CA) and K_w (FKW) are defined. Note that FKW is used, since this is a floating-point quantity. The initial (PHS) is set at an arbitrary value simply to initialize it. Of course, it would not be desirable to give the correct pH for the initial solution. (Why?) Next, the hydronium ion concentration (H) and the pH (PH) are calculated. The 2.303 factor in the pH calculation is needed to convert from base e to base ten logarithms. The current CA, H, and PH values are then output. Next, the absolute value of the difference between the former pH (PHS) and the current pH is compared to 10^{-8} by using an IF statement. The absolute value is used to avoid a negative difference. If the difference between the pH values is less than or equal to 10^{-8}, the program branches to the output of the end of calculation message. On the other hand, if the difference is greater than 10^{-8}, the former pH is set equal to the current pH (This serves to save the current pH value.) and the acid concentration is decremented tenfold by division by ten. Then the program branches back to the calculation loop for another pass through the loop. The process will continue until the IF statement provides for branching to the end of the program. This method is referred to as an IF loop or a calculation loop under control of an IF statement. This program is designed for a specific purpose and is self-contained. That is, no data cards are needed with it. Programs of this type are written on occasion, but generally a program that accomplishes some general type of calculation is more useful.

The following FORTRAN IV program is similar to the foregoing one except that by use of double precision variables the acid concentration can be varied until the pH is constant to 16 digits.

```
C PROGRAM TO CALCULATE THE PH OF HCL SOLUTIONS
C
C DECLARATION OF DOUBLE PRECISION VARIABLES
      DOUBLE PRECISION CA, PHS, FKW, H, PH
C INITIALIZATION OF VARIABLES
      DATA CA, PHS, FKW / .10, .09, 1.0D−14/
C OUTPUT OF DESCRIPTION AND HEADINGS
      WRITE (6, 10)
   10 FORMAT(1H1, 14HPH OF HCL SOLU/2HCA, 28X1HH,
      28X2HPH)
```

```
C  CALCULATION LOOP
      5 H = (CA + (CA**2 + 4.*FKW)**.5)/2.0
        PH = -DLOG10(H)
C  OUTPUT CALCULATED RESULTS
        WRITE (6, 20) CA, H, PH
     20 FORMAT(1Hb, D23.16, 6XD23.16, 6XD23.16)
C  COMPARISON OF CURRENT AND FORMER PH
        IF(DABS(PHS - PH) .LT. 1.0E-16) GO TO 2
C  SAVE CURRENT PH
        PHS = PH
C  DECREMENT THE ACID CONCENTRATION
        CA = CA/10.0
C  BRANCH BACK TO START OF CALCULATION LOOP
        GO TO 5
C  INDICATE THE END OF CALCULATIONS
      2 WRITE (6, 30)
     30 FORMAT(1Hb, 22HEND OF PH CALCULATIONS)
        CALL EXIT
        END
```

This program functions in a manner quite analogous to the previous FORTRAN II program. The first statement sets up the variables as double precision. The DATA statement initializes some of the variables. These values are stored as double precision numbers, for the variables are double precision. The descrip-

TABLE 5-1. Output of the pH Program

PH OF HCL SOLU

CA	H	PH
$1.0000000E-00$	$1.0000000E-00$	$0.0000000E-99$
$1.0000000E-01$	$1.0000000E-01$	$9.9981980E-01$
$1.0000000E-02$	$1.0000000E-02$	$1.9996396E-00$
$1.0000000E-03$	$1.0000001E-03$	$2.9994594E-00$
$1.0000000E-04$	$1.0000011E-04$	$3.9992788E-00$
$1.0000000E-05$	$1.0001002E-05$	$4.9990555E-00$
$1.0000000E-06$	$1.0099020E-06$	$5.9946404E-00$
$1.0000000E-07$	$1.6180347E-07$	$6.7897885E-00$
$1.0000000E-08$	$1.0512492E-07$	$6.9770369E-00$
$1.0000000E-09$	$1.0050134E-07$	$6.9965670E-00$
$1.0000000E-10$	$1.0005004E-07$	$6.9985214E-00$
$1.0000000E-11$	$1.0000504E-07$	$6.9987168E-00$
$1.0000000E-12$	$1.0000054E-07$	$6.9987364E-00$
$1.0000000E-13$	$1.0000009E-07$	$6.9987381E-00$
$1.0000000E-14$	$1.0000005E-07$	$6.9987386E-00$
$1.0000000E-15$	$1.0000004E-07$	$6.9987386E-00$

END OF PH CALCULATIONS

tion and headings are output via a WRITE statement. Note the printer control character in the FORMAT statement. The calculation loop uses an arithmetic statement to find H. The hierarchy of calculations is such that H is calculated as a double precision number. The pH is determined using the special library subroutine DLOG10, which is designed to calculate the base ten logarithms of double precision numbers. Additional special library functions are available on many computers. The computer specifications manual should be consulted for a complete description of the available functions. The comparison of the former and current pH is accomplished by a logical IF statement. Note the use of the special library subroutine DABS to find the absolute value of a double precision number. If the logical IF statement is .FALSE., the current pH is saved, the acid concentration is decremented, and the calculation loop is repeated. When the IF statement is .TRUE., the end of calculations message is recorded.

4. Output of the FORTRAN II program is given in Table 5-1 and the output of the FORTRAN IV program in Table 5-2. The differences between the calculated results seem to be due to truncation errors (see Appendix 1) and differences in the series used to calculate the logarithms in the library subrou-

TABLE 5-2. Output of pH Program

PH OF HCL SOLU

CA	H	PH
0.100000000000000D−00	0.1000000000001000D−00	0.9999999999995657D−00
0.100000000000000D−01	0.1000000000100000D−01	0.1999999999956571D+01
0.100000000000000D−02	0.1000000010000000D−02	0.2999999995657055D+01
0.100000000000000D−03	0.1000000999999000D−03	0.3999999565706170D+01
0.100000000000000D−04	0.1000099990002000D−04	0.4999956577064779D+01
0.100000000000000D−05	0.1009901951359279D−05	0.5995720788643735D+01
0.100000000000000D−06	0.1618033988749895D−06	0.6791012359750012D+01
0.100000000000000D−07	0.1051249219725039D−06	0.6978294313542888D+01
0.100000000000000D−08	0.1005012499921876D−06	0.6997828536638184D+01
0.100000000000000D−09	0.1000500124999992D−06	0.6999782852768096D+01
0.100000000000000D−10	0.1000050001250000D−06	0.6999978285275914D+01
0.100000000000000D−11	0.1000005000012500D−06	0.6999997828527590D+01
0.100000000000000D−12	0.1000000500000125D−06	0.6999999782852759D+01
0.100000000000000D−13	0.1000000050000001D−06	0.6999999978285276D+01
0.100000000000000D−14	0.1000000005000000D−06	0.6999999997828528D+01
0.100000000000000D−15	0.1000000000500000D−06	0.6999999999782853D+01
0.100000000000000D−16	0.1000000000050000D−06	0.6999999999978285D+01
0.100000000000000D−17	0.1000000000005000D−06	0.6999999999997829D+01
0.100000000000000D−18	0.1000000000000500D−06	0.6999999999999783D+01
0.100000000000000D−19	0.1000000000000050D−06	0.6999999999999978D+01
0.100000000000000D−20	0.1000000000000005D−06	0.6999999999999998D+01
0.100000000000000D−21	0.1000000000000001D−06	0.7000000000000000D+01
0.100000000000000D−22	0.1000000000000000D−06	0.7000000000000000D+01

END OF PH CALCULATIONS

tines. Furthermore, the pH values of 7 output by the FORTRAN IV program are due to the extremely weak solutions being used in the calculations. Of course, these are only hypothetical solutions.

EXAMPLE 2

1. The problem is to write a program to add two matrices A and B and then multiply the sum matrix by a constant. (See Chapter 9 for a discussion of matrix algebra.) From a programming point of view, the problem is to read in the matrices and constant, accomplish the calculations, and output the resulting matrix.

2. A flow chart of a method to solve the above problem appears in Figure 5-2.

3. A FORTRAN program written from the flow chart is

```
C  MATRIX PROGRAM
        DIMENSION A(10, 10), B(10, 10)
        READ 5, CONST          or READ (5, 5)*
     5  FORMAT(E14.7)
        READ 10, N, M, ((A(I, J), J = 1, M), I = 1, N) or READ (5, 10)
        READ 10, N, M, ((B(I, J), J = 1, M), I = 1, N) or READ (5, 10)
    10  FORMAT(I2, 2XI2/(E14.7, 2XE14.7, 2XE14.7, 2XE14.7))
C  ADD A AND B
        DO 1 J = 1, M
        DO 2 I = 1, N
     2  A(I, J) = A(I, J) + B(I, J)
     1  CONTINUE
C  MULT A BY CONSTANT
        DO 100 J = 1, M
        DO 200 I = 1, N
   200  A(I, J) = CONST*A(I, J)
   100  CONTINUE
C  OUTPUT RESULT
        PUNCH 20,((A(I, J), I = 1, N), J = 1, M)        or WRITE (7, 20)
    20  FORMAT(5E14.7)
        CALL EXIT
        END
```

The DIMENSION statement defines the maximum size of the two matrices involved. The elements of the sum matrix can be stored in one of these two matrices, so it is not necessary to waste storage by defining a sum matrix. Of

---

* Some of the programs are written with both FORTRAN II and FORTRAN IV keywords in statements in which there is a difference between the two versions.

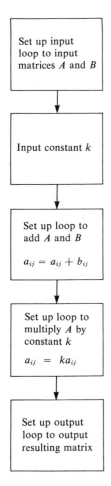

FIG. 5-2. Flow chart for matrix addition and multiplication by a constant.

course, if it is desirable to retain the original matrices in storage, a sum matrix should be defined. The DIMENSION statement can be altered to accommodate any size of matrix by changing the maximum subscript values. The only limitation is the amount of available core storage. The constant is read in from a card in scientific notation form ($\pm n.nnnnnnnE\pm nn$), which can be accommodated by the FORMAT specification E14.7. Next, matrix A is read in from cards according to FORMAT 10. Notice that the first card read in contains an N value, indicating the number of rows and an M value, indicating the number of columns of the matrix A. These values are used to set up the read-in loop in which A is read row by row. According to FORMAT 10, there are four elements per card, and each element is in scientific notation form. Matrix B

is then read in in the same manner. Notice that the same FORMAT is used as for *A*. The technique of reading in the parameters for a read-in loop prior to the execution of the loop is a good way to input arrays and matrices with sizes that depend on the particular data being used with the program. In this manner, a program can be written in a general form in order to be used with various forms of data. Next, a nested DO loop is set up to calculate the sum of the two matrices. Notice that each time through the loop a given element of the matrix *A* is replaced by the corresponding element of the sum matrix (see Section 9-1). The next step involves another nested DO loop in which the sum matrix, which is stored in *A* and thus referred to as *A*, is multiplied by the constant factor. The addition and multiplication by the constant could have been accomplished in one nested DO loop using a statement such as

$$A(I, J) = CONST*(A(I, J) + B(I, J))$$

but the example is written to illustrate the steps separately. Finally, the resulting matrix is output in an output loop column by column according to FORMAT 20.

4. Input and output for this program are shown in Table 5-3.

TABLE 5-3. Input and Output of the Matrix Algebra Program

Input				
2.0000000E−00				
04 04				
1.0000000E−00	8.0000000E−00	2.7000000E 01	6.4000000E 01	
1.0000000E−00	2.0000000E−00	3.0000000E−00	4.0000000E−00	
1.0000000E−00	1.0000000E−00	1.0000000E−00	1.0000000E−00	
1.0000000E−00	4.0000000E−00	9.0000000E−00	1.6000000E 01	
04 04				
1.0000000E−00	1.0000000E−00	1.0000000E−00	1.0000000E−00	
1.0000000E−00	2.0000000E−00	3.0000000E−00	4.0000000E−00	
1.0000000E−00	4.0000000E−00	9.0000000E−00	1.6000000E 01	
1.0000000E−00	8.0000000E−00	2.7000000E−00	6.4000000E 01	
Output				
4.0000000E−00	4.0000000E−00	4.0000000E−00	4.0000000E−00	1.8000000E+01
8.0000000E−00	1.0000000E+01	2.4000000E+01	5.6000000E+01	1.2000000E+01
2.0000000E+01	7.2000000E+01	1.3000000E+02	1.6000000E+01	3.4000000E+01
1.6000000E+02				

EXAMPLE 3

1. In statistics, the coefficient of linear correlation serves as a measure of the strength of the linear relationship that exists between two variables. That is, it serves as an expression of how well two variables are related in a linear manner to one another. Occasionally it is used to express the "correlation" between

two sets of data that were collected independently. For example, if two analysts independently carried out replicate analyses using the same set of samples, the "correlation" between the two sets of results could be expressed by the correlation coefficient. A high value for the correlation coefficient (approaching one) would indicate good correlation, while a low value (approaching zero) would indicate poor correlation. However, no quantitative judgment can be made from the value of the correlation coefficient. The linear correlation coefficient can be calculated by

$$r = \frac{n \sum x_i y_i - (\sum x_i)(\sum y_i)}{\{[n \sum x_i^2 - (\sum x_i)^2][n \sum y_i^2 - (\sum y_i)^2]\}^{1/2}}$$

where x_i and y_i are corresponding members of a set of x and y values. The summations are from $i = 1$ to $i = n$, where n is the number of pairs of x and y values.

The problem is to write a program that will determine the coefficient of correlation for a given set of x and y values. The program will have to be written to read in the data, compute the various summations, and then calculate the coefficient.

2. A flow chart for the above problem is given in Figure 5-3.

3. A FORTRAN program written from the flow chart is

```
C  PROGRAM TO FIND COEFF OF CORRELATION
        DIMENSION X(25), Y(25)
        READ 10, N, (X(I), Y(I), I = 1, N)        or READ (5, 10)
    10  FORMAT(I2,/(E14.7, 2XE14.7))
C  INITIALIZATION
        SUMXY = 0.0
        SUMX = 0.0
        SUMY = 0.0
        SUMX2 = 0.0
        SUMY2 = 0.0
C  SUMMATION CALCULATIONS
        DO 5 I = 1, N
        SUMX = SUMX + X(I)
        SUMY = SUMY + Y(I)
        SUMXY = SUMXY + X(I)*Y(I)
        SUMX2 = SUMX2 + X(I)**2
        SUMY2 = SUMY2 + Y(I)**2
     5  CONTINUE
        FN = N
C  COEFF CALCULATION
        R = (FN*SUMXY - SUMX*SUMY)/SQRTF((FN*SUMX2
           - SUMX**2)*(FN*SUMY2 - SU
    1MY**2))          or use SQRT
```

C OUTPUT
      TYPE 20, R   or WRITE (6, 20)
  20 FORMAT(20HCORRELATION COEFF = E14.7)
        or (1Hb, 20H, etc. for printer control)
      CALL EXIT
      END

The DIMENSION statement defines the maximum values of the subscripts of the arrays X(I) and Y(I). This maximum subscript can be changed to accommodate any number of x and y values. The only limitation is the amount of storage available. The arrays are read in from cards according to FORMAT 10. Note that N, the number of sets of x and y values, is read in from the first card.

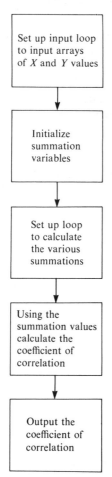

Fig. 5-3. Flow chart for the calculation of the coefficient of correlation.

This provides for the establishment of an input loop to read in the two arrays. As can be seen from the specifications in FORMAT 10, one set of x and y values is to be read in from each data card. Next, the variables to be used in the determination of the summations are initialized. The reason for this is that when the summations are carried out in the calculation loop, the initial values for the variable names used for the sums must be zeros. The calculation loop is a DO loop in which all required summations are calculated. Notice how the DO loop indexing parameter is used in the subscripts of the arrays to refer to the various members of the arrays. Finally, the coefficient of correlation is calculated and output.

4. As an example of the input and output of this program, consider the determination of the coefficient of correlation for a set of x and y values corresponding to the results of chloride ion analyses accomplished by two analysts using the same set of samples as unknowns. The data involved are as follows:

Unknown Chloride	Percent Chloride Ion	
Sample Number	Analyst x	Analyst y
1	11.65	11.60
2	12.37	12.34
3	18.58	18.54
4	10.52	10.49
5	13.75	13.74

The input and output for this data, using the program given above, are shown in Table 5-4.

TABLE 5-4. Input and Output of Correlation Coefficient Program

```
Input
05
    1.1650000E  01    1.1600000E  01
    1.2370000E  01    1.2340000E  01
    1.8580000E  01    1.8540000E  01
    1.0520000E  01    1.0490000E  01
    1.3750000E  01    1.3740000E  01
Output
CORRELATION  COEFF = 9.9998887E−01
```

5-2. PROGRAMMING TIPS AND SUGGESTIONS.

When a program is written, it should be designed to be as general as possible so that various types of data and calculating situations can be accommodated. A general program will usually be more useful. Once a program has been written and prepared for use on the computer, the punched cards should be checked for punching errors. If the program fails to run correctly, there are generally two possible causes: (1) errors in the use of the FORTRAN language and (2) errors in the logic of the program. Most syntax errors or errors in the use of the language are detected by the compiler during compilation and an error message is output. The error message is coded; thus a list of the error codes is needed to determine the nature of the error. (A list of error codes for FORTRAN II D appears in Appendix 1.) To avoid the time-consuming problem of correcting a simple syntax error after compilation has been attempted, it is good practice to double check the punched cards containing your program before compilation. Some common errors that may occur are listed below.

1. Failure to define a variable before it is used in a statement in which the value is needed. A variable can be defined by an arithmetic statement or an input statement.

2. Mixing mode (fixed and floating) in an arithmetic statement.

3. Using the same statement number more than one time.

4. Failing to give a statement the same statement number used to refer to it by some other statement.

5. Starting a FORTRAN statement in a card column before the seventh column.

6. Using the same variable name for more than one variable. (Subscripted variables are acceptable.)

7. Using incorrect subscripts for a subscripted variable.

8. The number of open parentheses does not equal the number of closed parentheses.

9. Incorrectly forming an arithmetic statement.

10. Using two arithmetic operation symbols in sequence or omitting an arithmetic symbol.

11. Improper alteration of a DO loop index or improper entry or exit from a DO loop.

12. Failure to initialize variables that require initialization.

13. Allowing the parameter of a computed GO TO statement to exceed the number of possible statement numbers used in the statement.

14. Failure to use a comma in a position where required.

15. Using insufficient maximum subscript values for subscripted variables.

16. Use of an invalid argument in a subroutine.

17. Incorrectly formed FORMAT statement. This is a very common error, so be sure that the data and the FORMAT specifications agree.

18. Using a fixed-point variable name to refer to a floating-point number or vice versa. This, too, is a very common error.

19. Incorrect arrangement of data cards or improper recording of data.

20. Failure to have the Hollerith character count agree with the number

of Hollerith characters used. Remember that blanks are counted as characters. Again, this is a common error.

21. Incorrect order of FORTRAN statements. Nonlogical arrangement of statements or placing executable statements before statements that must precede all executable statements.

If no language error or mistake similar to those listed above can be found in a program that does not function correctly, then a logic error in the program is the most probable cause of trouble. To find a logic error, the flow chart should be checked. Another approach is to mentally trace the processing of some simple data through the program. This tracing process, if done carefully, usually will help in finding the logic error. If the program seems to give incorrect results and an error cannot be found, a set of data for which the result is known can be used to check the functioning of the program. If the error still cannot be found, the final possible solution is to start over and rewrite the program. As mentioned previously, a great deal of time can be saved by carefully checking the logic of the program and the prepared statements before an attempt is made to run the program.

5-3. STUDENT PROGRAMS.

Each chapter in the second part of this book contains one or more student programs; that is, suggested programs that the student can write and that may be useful for certain applications. It is not necessary to write all of these programs, but most can be quite useful for the solution of problems occurring in the laboratory or lecture. The student is encouraged to write programs of any nature for use in solving any problems that appear in his study of chemistry. Furthermore, any of the student programs can be altered in order to solve a problem of specific interest to the student.

5-4. STUDENT PROGRAM 5-1.

Write a program that will carry out the calculations for a gravimetric or volumetric quantitative analysis. The experimental data and constants can be input from data cards. The first data card can contain a parameter value to be used with a computed GO TO statement so that the appropriate calculation steps for gravimetric or volumetric calculations can be carried out. That is, the computed GO TO statement can be used to allow for the branching to the gravimetric calculations or the volumetric calculations. In either case, the calculations should involve the determination of the percentage of the sought species. The data can be input in the form of subscripted variables using an appropriate input loop. A number indicating the number of sets of data can be read in from one of the initial data cards. A DO loop can be set up to calculate the percentages. Once the percentages have been determined, another DO loop can be set up to calculate the mean value. Since the standard deviation can be used as a measure of precision, the program should include the calculation of the standard deviation. This can be conveniently calculated by

$$ s = \left[\frac{\sum x_i^2 - (\sum x_i)^2/n}{n - 1} \right]^{1/2} $$

where the x_i values correspond to the various percentages calculated from n sets of data and the summations are from $i = 1$ to $i = n$. In order to find the standard deviation, the program must include calculation loops to determine the required summations. If desired, the program can include the calculation of the confidence limit of the mean. Finally, the program should be designed to output the percentages, the mean, and the standard deviation along with appropriate commentary. The output can be recorded by a printer, typewriter, card punch, or magnetic tape, depending on the nature of the computer installation being used.

Once a program has been prepared for compilation, the way in which the processing of the program can be carried out depends on how the computer installation you will be using is set up. Some installations provide an open computer laboratory in which the students operate the computer. In such a case, the student must learn to operate the computer and should obtain appropriate operation instructions. Certain installations without open laboratories have established procedures that allow the student to requisition a computer job. Generally the requisition procedure involves the submission of the prepared program, plus a description of the type of computer job required. (See Appendix 2.) Such computer jobs are usually carried out at night or at times when the computer is available. Completed jobs, or a description of the problems that occurred with the job, are returned to the student within a day or two.

CHAPTER 6

DATA MANIPULATION

AND FUNCTION

EVALUATION

6-1. FUNCTION EVALUATION.

The evaluation of algebraic functions is often required in theoretical and experimental chemistry. A function is an algebraic relationship, involving a variable, that has one value corresponding to each value of the variable. Standard notation for a function is

$$y = f(x)$$

where x is the independent variable related to the dependent variable y by the function. The value of y depends on the values of x. Many functions are used in chemistry and are either based on fundamental definitions or on theory. For example, the function for density, $D = M/V$, is based on a definition, whereas the equation of state of perfect gas, $PV = nRT$, is derived from theory. In either case, only certain domains of values apply to the function; that is, the variables can assume only certain physically meaningful values. Quantities such as negative volume or negative mass have no physical significance and are never used.

Functions are represented in three ways: algebraic relationships, graphical form, and tabular form. The particular manner in which a function is expressed depends on the way in which the function was developed and on the way it is to be used. Furthermore, it is often necessary to change from one functional representation form to another, for example, from experimentally determined tabular form to a graphical form. In a given instance, one form of a function is usually more useful than another form. Often a computer program can be used in the transformation of the forms of functions. From an experimental point of view, the usual sequence of transformation is from tabular to graphical or from tabular to algebraic. The plotting of tabular data can be accomplished with special plotting subroutines, and some computers are equipped with plotting machines as output devices. The techniques involved in this type of transformation will not be discussed. The transformation of tabular data to an algebraic expression is called curve fitting and is discussed in Chapter 10. The conversion of an algebraic expression to a tabulation of independent variables and dependent variables is often desirable for calculation purposes. The techniques involved in this type of conversion are the main concern of this chapter.

The process of converting from an algebraic form of a function to a tabular form involves finding the desirable algebraic function, ascertaining the values of the constants, and then determining the values of the dependent variable that correspond to the values of the independent variable. For example, consider how the pressure of a fixed number of moles of gas at a constant temperature varies as the volume is changed. As a desirable algebraic function expressing a relationship between pressure and volume, the Dieterici equation of a state of a gas can be used.

$$Pe^{(an/VRT)}(V - nb) = nRT$$

Here P is the pressure in atmospheres, V is the volume in liters, T is the Kelvin temperature, R is the gas constant with appropriate units, n is the number of moles of gas, and a and b are empirical constants that depend on the specific gas being considered. Solving the above equation for pressure gives

$$P = \frac{nRTe^{(-an/VRT)}}{V - nb}.$$

Using this relationship, a program can be written to calculate P as a function of V for a specific number of moles of a given gas at a constant temperature. The values of the pressure can be calculated for the various volumes by starting at the desired initial volume and incrementing by the desired volume increment. Of course, all values for the constants, the initial value of the volume, and the increment value must be established before starting the calculation loop. A program to accomplish the evaluation of the function is shown below.

```
C PROGRAM TO CALCULATE P AS A FUNCTION OF V
        FUNCF(X) = (FN*R*T*EXPF((−A*FN)/(X*R*T)))/(X − FN*B)
            or use EXP
        READ 5                          or READ (5, 5)
        READ 10, FN, R, T, A, B         or READ (5, 10)
```

```
        READ 20, M, DELV, V              or READ (5, 20)
        TYPE 5                           or WRITE (6, 5)
        TYPE 6, FN, T                    or WRITE (6, 6)
        DO 1 I = 1, M
        P = FUNCF(V)
        TYPE 30, P, V                    or WRITE (6, 30)
     1  V = V + DELV
     6  FORMAT(16HNUMBER OF MOLES E14.7, 1X 12HTEMPERA-
           TURE E14.7) or (1Hb, 16H, etc.)
    10  FORMAT(E14.7, 1XE14.7, 1XE14.7, 1XE14.7, 1XE14.7)
     5  FORMAT(25H                                 )
           or (1Hb, 25H, etc.)
    20  FORMAT(I3, 1XE14.7, 1XE14.7)
    30  FORMAT(4HP = E11.4, 5X4HV = E11.4)       or (1Hb, 4H, etc.)
        END
```

An example of input and output for this program is shown in Table 6-1.

The tabulation of values of the independent and dependent variables of a function is often advisable because the tables can be quite useful for subsequent calculations. A general program for the evaluation of functions similar to the program given above can be devised. A flow chart for such a program appears in Figure 6-1.

6-2. STUDENT PROGRAM 6-1.

Write a general FORTRAN program that will tabulate values of the independent and dependent variables for a function like $y = f(x)$. Design the program according to one of the flow charts shown in Figure 6-1. The calculation loop can be a DO loop or controlled by an IF statement. Notice that the program given above is written according to the general pattern. Of course, only the loop and some of the input and output statements in the general program can be written in a strictly general form. The definition of the function, the constant input and the DIMENSION statement, and the FORMAT statement must be written to correspond to the specific function.

6-3. MULTIVARIABLE EVALUATIONS AND TABULATIONS.

Occasionally it is necessary to prepare tabulations of the variables of a function involving more than two variables. This situation could easily be handled by writing the program so that it contains nested DO loops. Thus one variable could be held constant, while the values of the other are determined over the

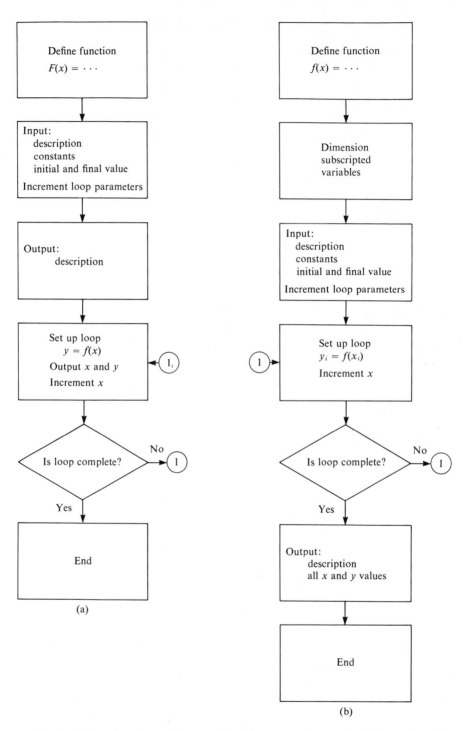

FIG. 6-1. Flow chart for function evaluation (a) without subscripted variables and (b) with subscripted variables.

TABLE 6-1. Input and Output for the Function Evaluation Program

Input
CARBON DIOXIDE
  1.0000000+00   8.2030000E−02   2.9800000E+02   3.6000000E+00   4.2800000E−02
030   1.0000000E+00   1.0000000E+00

Output
CARBON DIOXIDE

NUMBER OF MOLES	1.0000000E−00	TEMPERATURE	2.9800000E+02
P = 2.2040E+01	V = 1.0000E−00		
P = 1.1603E+01	V = 2.0000E−00		
P = 7.8702E−00	V = 3.0000E−00		
P = 5.9540E−00	V = 4.0000E−00		
P = 4.7880E−00	V = 5.0000E−00		
P = 4.0039E−00	V = 6.0000E−00		
P = 3.4404E−00	V = 7.0000E−00		
P = 3.0160E−00	V = 8.0000E−00		
P = 2.6847E−00	V = 9.0000E−00		
P = 2.4191E−00	V = 1.0000E+01		
P = 2.2012E−00	V = 1.1000E+01		
P = 2.0194E−00	V = 1.2000E+01		
P = 1.8653E−00	V = 1.3000E+01		
P = 1.7330E−00	V = 1.4000E+01		
P = 1.6183E−00	V = 1.5000E+01		
P = 1.5178E−00	V = 1.6000E+01		
P = 1.4291E−00	V = 1.7000E+01		
P = 1.3501E−00	V = 1.8000E+01		
P = 1.2795E−00	V = 1.9000E+01		
P = 1.2158E−00	V = 2.0000E+01		
P = 1.1582E−00	V = 2.1000E+01		
P = 1.1058E−00	V = 2.2000E+01		
P = 1.0580E−00	V = 2.3000E+01		
P = 1.0141E−00	V = 2.4000E+01		
P = 9.7372E−01	V = 2.5000E+01		
P = 9.3642E−01	V = 2.6000E+01		
P = 9.0187E−01	V = 2.7000E+01		
P = 8.6978E−01	V = 2.8000E+01		
P = 8.3989E−01	V = 2.9000E+01		
P = 8.1199E−01	V = 3.0000E+01		

desired range. Then the first variable could be incremented, and the others could be calculated using this new incremented value. This could be repeated as often as desired and could be extended to several variables. To illustrate, consider the evaluation of pressure as a function of volume for varying temperatures of a gas using the Dieterici equation of state. A program designed to produce this tabulation follows.

```
C PROGRAM TO FIND PRESSURE AND VOLUME AT VARIOUS
          TEMPERATURES
      FUNCF(X) = (FN*R*T*EXPF((−A*FN)/(X*R*T)))/
      (X − FN*B)          or use EXP
      READ 10, FN, R, A, B                      or READ (5, 10)
      READ 20, N, M, T, DELT, V, DELV           or READ (5, 10)
      VC = V
      DO 2 J = 1, N
      TYPE 30, T                                or WRITE (6, 30)
      DO 1 I = 1, M
      P = FUNCF(VC)
      TYPE 40, P, VC                            or WRITE (6, 40)
      VC = VC + DELV
    1 CONTINUE
      T = T + DELT
      VC = V
    2 CONTINUE
   10 FORMAT(F6.4, 1XE8.3, 1XF7.5, 1XF7.5)
   20 FORMAT(I3, 1XI3, 1XF5.1, 1XF3.1, 1XF5.3, 1XF5.3)
   30 FORMAT(/E11.4, 8H DEGREES, /29HPRESSURE(ATM)
          VOLUME(LITERS)) or (1Hb, E11.4, etc.)
   40 FORMAT(E11.4, 3XE11.4) or (1Hb, E11.4, etc.)
      CALL EXIT
      END
```

Table 6-2 shows typical input and output for this program.

Problems

The following suggested problems can be solved with the function evaluation program discussed in Section 6-1. Some will require modification of the basic program, for they involve multivariable evaluations. Each problem has a brief theoretical discussion and a description of some of the programming steps involved. However, the student is encouraged to apply any of the student programs in the book to any problem that may be of interest to him.

1. Van der Waals equation of state for a gas is

$$\frac{P + an^2}{V^2} (V - nb) = nRT$$

where P is the pressure in atmospheres, V is the volume in liters, T is the absolute temperature, n is the number of moles, R is the gas constant, and a and b are empirical constants, which must be evaluated for a specific gas. The equation

TABLE 6-2. Input and Output for the Multivariable
Function Evaluation Program

Input
0.0200   8.023E−2   3.60000   0.042800
004   004   285.0   5.0   0.450   0.025

Output
2.8500E+02 DEGREES

PRESSURE(ATM)	VOLUME(LITERS)
1.0110E−00	4.5000E−01
9.5812E−01	4.7500E−01
9.1043E−01	5.0000E−01
8.6727E−01	5.2500E−01

2.9000E+02 DEGREES

PRESSURE(ATM)	VOLUME(LITERS)
1.0289E−00	4.5000E−01
9.7504E−01	4.7500E−01
9.2651E−01	5.0000E−01
8.8258E−01	5.2500E−01

2.9500E+02 DEGREES

PRESSURE(ATM)	VOLUME(LITERS)
1.0468E−00	4.5000E−01
9.9196E−01	4.7500E−01
9.4258E−01	5.0000E−01
8.9788E−01	5.2500E−01

3.0000E+02 DEGREES

PRESSURE(ATM)	VOLUME(LITERS)
1.0646E−00	4.5000E−01
1.0088E−00	4.7500E−01
9.5865E−01	5.0000E−01
9.1319E−01	5.2500E−10

---

can be rearranged to express the pressure as a function of the other variables. Write a program to determine the pressure as a function of volume for n moles of gas at temperature T. The values of n, T, a, and b can be read in from a card. The initial volume and volume increment can also be input from a card. Many texts have extensive tabulations of the Van der Waals constants, a and b. Following is a list of these constants for a few gases.

Gas	a ($l^2\ atm\ mole^{-2}$)	b ($l\ mole^{-1}$)
Ar	1.35	0.0322
H_2	0.246	0.0266
H_2O	5.47	0.0305
CO_2	3.60	0.0428

2. The molar heat capacity at constant pressure of a substance is the amount of heat required to raise the temperature of one mole of the substance

one degree Celsius at a fixed pressure. The molar heat capacities of gases are functions of temperature and can be evaluated from the general expression

$$C_p = a + bT + cT^2$$

where T is the absolute temperature and a, b, and c are empirical constants that depend upon the gas being considered. Constants for several gases for the 300 to 1500 °K range are as follows:

Gas	a	b	c
O_2	6.148	3.102×10^{-3}	-9.23×10^{-7}
N_2	6.524	1.250×10^{-3}	-0.01×10^{-7}
CO_2	6.214	10.396×10^{-3}	-35.45×10^{-7}
H_2O	7.256	2.298×10^{-3}	2.83×10^{-7}

Write a program to read a data card containing the name of the gas, the constants a, b, and c, and the initial and final value of the temperature. Design the program to calculate the heat capacity as a function of temperature and print out the results. Vary the temperature from the initial value to the final value by a convenient increment, such as ten degrees. An IF statement can be used to control the incrementation.

3. The expression for radioactive decay as a function of time is

$$n = n_0 e^{-kt}$$

where n is the number of nuclei at time t, n_0 is the initial number of nuclei, and k is the radioactive decay constant that is characteristic of the element involved. The decay constant is related to the half-life of a specific nuclide by the equation

$$k = \frac{\ln 2}{t_{1/2}}.$$

The half-lives of radioactive nuclides vary widely, and are expressed in units of seconds, minutes, hours, days, or years.

Write a program to calculate the number of grams of a radioactive element as a function of time. Read in the initial number of grams, the half-life, the units of the half-life, and the name of the element along with its mass number. Design the program to calculate the various values of n using one tenth half-life increments $(t_{1/2}/10)$ up to ten half-lives. Punch out the name of the element and the half-life on one card. Then punch the n and t values on subsequent cards. A typical input card could be

01.00	6.70E00	YEARS	RADIUM 228
grams	half-life	units	nuclide

4. The equation giving the wavelength, λ, of the photon emitted or absorbed upon transition of an electron between energy levels of hydrogenlike atoms according to the Bohr model is

$$\frac{1}{\lambda} = R \left(\frac{1}{n^2} - \frac{1}{m^2} \right)$$

where λ is the wavelength in centimeters, R is the Rydberg constant, 109,677.58 cm^{-1}, and n and m are quantum numbers corresponding to the energy levels of the electron. The lines of the emission spectra of atomic hydrogen correspond to the possible quantum level changes and can be classified into series of lines, depending on the value of n. The important series are

Lyman series	$n = 1$	m greater than 1
Balmer series	$n = 2$	m greater than 2
Paschen series	$n = 3$	m greater than 3
Pfund series	$n = 4$	m greater than 4

Write a program to calculate the wave numbers, $1/\lambda$ cm^{-1}, the wavelengths, λ cm, the frequency, $\nu = c/\lambda$, where c is the velocity of light, 2.9979×10^{10} cm/sec, and the energy, $E = h\nu$, where h is Planck's constant, 6.6256×10^{-27} erg sec, for the lines of the four series corresponding to m varying from $n + 1$ to 10. Output the results with appropriate designation. If desired, the program can be shortened to calculate only one of the above factors.

5. The Debye-Hückel equation used to approximate the activity coefficient of an ion is

$$\log (f_i) = \frac{0.5085Z_i^2\mu^{1/2}}{1 + 0.3281\alpha_i\mu^{1/2}}$$

where f_i = activity coefficient of species i
Z_i = the absolute value of the charge on species i
μ = the ionic strength of the solution
α_i = the empirically derived diameter of the hydrated ion in Angstrom units.

The two numerical constants apply to aqueous solutions at 25 °C. Table 6-3 shows some ions and the corresponding α_i values:

TABLE 6-3. Some Ionic Sizes

Ion	Ion Size
	$\alpha_i(A)$
H_3O^+	9
Li^+	6
Na^+, IO_3^-, OAc^-	4
K^+, Cl^-, Br^-, I^-, CN^-, NO_2^-, NO_3^-	3
NH_4^+, Ag^+	2.5
Mg^{++}	8
Ca^{++}, Cu^{++}, Zn^{++}, Mn^{++}, Ni^{++}, Co^{++}	6
Ba^{++}, Cd^{++}	5
Hg_2^{++}, $SO_4^=$, $CrO_4^=$	4
Al^{3+}, Fe^{3+}	9
PO_4^{3-}	4

Write a program to tabulate activity coefficients at ionic strengths of 10^{-3}, 5×10^{-3}, 10^{-2}, 5×10^{-2}, and 10^{-1} for the various ions given in the table. A subscripted variable could be used for manipulation of the various ion sizes. The calculations could be accomplished by a loop. Output a descriptive heading, as well as ionic strength values. Then output a table giving the ion size and the activity coefficients corresponding to the various ionic strengths. The specification F6.3 would suffice for the activity coefficients.

6. When dealing with equilibria in the solution phase, it is often desirable to determine concentrations of solution species as a function of the concentration of some specific species or some solution condition, such as pH. The procedure involved in such calculations can be generalized. For example, consider an aqueous solution of the weak acid HA. The equilibrium involved is

$$HA + H_2O = H_3O^+ + A^-.$$

Some quantitative relationships between species in solution are the equilibrium constant expression

$$K_a = \frac{[H_3O^+][A^-]}{[HA]}$$

and the mass balance

$$C_{HA} = [HA] + [A^-]$$

where C_{HA} is the initial acid concentration. Let α_0 and α_1 be the fractions of the total acid concentration, C_{HA}, which are in the form of HA and A$^-$, respectively. Thus

$$\alpha_0 = \frac{[HA]}{C_{HA}} \quad \text{and} \quad \alpha_1 = \frac{[A^-]}{C_{HA}}.$$

Using the equilibrium expression and the mass balance, the fractions can be expressed in terms of the equilibrium constant and the $[H_3O^+]$ only.

$$\alpha_0 = \frac{[HA]}{C_{HA}} = \frac{\dfrac{[H_3O^+][A^-]}{K_a}}{\dfrac{[H_3O^+][A^-]}{K_a} + [A^-]} = \frac{[H_3O^+]}{[H_3O^+] + K_a}$$

$$\alpha_1 = \frac{[A^-]}{C_{HA}} = \frac{[A^-]}{\dfrac{[H_3O^+][A^-]}{K_a} + [A^-]} = \frac{K_a}{[H_3O^+] + K_a}$$

At a given pH, the fractions can be calculated and the concentrations of the species can be determined if C_{HA} is known. That is,

$$[A^-] = C_{HA}\alpha_1 \quad \text{and} \quad [HA] = C_{HA}\alpha_0.$$

These considerations apply equally well to any polyprotic weak acid solution, any weak base solution, or any solution containing a complex ion. The following general equations can be derived for a polyprotic acid system:

$$\alpha_0 = \frac{[H_3O^+]^n}{D} = \frac{[H_nA]}{C_a}$$

$$\alpha_1 = \frac{(K_1[H_3O^+]^{n-1})}{D} = \frac{[H_{n-1}A^-]}{C_a}$$

$$\alpha_2 = \frac{(K_1K_2[H_3O^+]^{n-2})}{D} = \frac{[H_{n-2}A^{--}]}{C_a}$$

$$\cdot \quad \cdot \quad \cdot \quad \cdot \quad \cdot \quad \cdot \quad \cdot \quad \cdot \quad \cdot \quad \cdot \quad \cdot \quad \cdot \quad \cdot$$

$$\alpha_i = \frac{(K_1K_2 \cdots K_i[H_3O^+]^{n-i})}{D} = \frac{[H_{n-i}A^{-i}]}{C_a}$$

$$\cdot \quad \cdot \quad \cdot \quad \cdot \quad \cdot \quad \cdot \quad \cdot \quad \cdot \quad \cdot \quad \cdot \quad \cdot \quad \cdot \quad \cdot$$

$$\alpha_n = \frac{(K_1K_2 \cdots K_n)}{D} = \frac{[A^{-n}]}{C_a}$$

$$D = [H_3O^+]^n + K_1[H_3O^+]^{n-1} + K_1K_2[H_3O^+]^{n-2} + \cdots + K_1K_2 \cdots K_n.$$

The K values are the corresponding acid equilibrium constants. A similar set of equations could be used for a solution of a complex ion. The differences would be that the $[H_3O^+]$ are replaced by ligand concentration, the K values would be the various instability constants of the complex ion equilibria, and C_a would correspond to the total metal ion concentration.

Write a program to calculate α values as a function of pH or ligand concentration for any acid or complex ion. For the acid, variation of the pH from 1 to 14 would be desirable. The various parts of the α values can be calculated in appropriate DO loops. The constants, and the initial and final values of the independent variable, can be read in from cards. Output a tabulation of α values and pH values, or ligand concentrations, along with descriptive commentary. The tabulation can be used to determine concentrations of various species corresponding to a specific initial concentration of parent species. The program can be used with any system desired. The required constants for some systems are given below.

Phosphoric acid H_3PO_4	$K_1 = 7.5 \times 10^{-3}$, $K_2 = 6.2 \times 10^{-8}$, $K_3 = 4.8 \times 10^{-13}$
Oxalic acid HOOCCOOH	$K_1 = 6.5 \times 10^{-2}$, $K_2 = 6.1 \times 10^{-5}$
Ethylenediamminetetra-acetic acid	$K_1 = 10^{-2}$, $K_2 = 2.14 \times 10^{-3}$, $K_3 = 6.9 \times 10^{-7}$, $K_4 = 5.5 \times 10^{-11}$
Tetrammine zinc ion (instability constants)	$K_4 = 1.52 \times 10^2$, $K_3 = 1.79 \times 10^2$, $K_2 = 2.00 \times 10^2$, $K_1 = 9.09 \times 10^1$

CHAPTER 7

EVALUATION OF ROOTS

OF EQUATIONS

7-1. ALGORITHMIC DETERMINATION OF ROOTS.

The evaluation of functions is straightforward and involves direct calculations; however, the reverse problem is often encountered. That is, given the function $y = f(x)$, what are the values of x corresponding to $y = 0$? These values of x are called the roots of the equation $f(x) = 0$. In the following discussion, numerical methods that provide means for the approximation of the roots of an equation will be considered. The roots of some types of equations are easily determined. For example, the roots of a quadratic equation, $ax^2 + bx + c = 0$, can be calculated using the familiar quadratic algorithm

$$x = \frac{-b \pm (b^2 - 4ac)^{1/2}}{2a}.$$

A program can easily be written to calculate the roots of a quadratic equation with this algorithm. Of course, the roots can be real or complex. To find the nature of the roots, the quantity $b^2 - 4ac$, called the discriminant, can be tested to see if it is negative or positive. If it is negative, the roots will be complex; and if it is positive, the roots can be calculated using the algorithm. For complex roots, the roots can be calculated by

$$\text{Complex roots} = \frac{-b}{2a} \pm \frac{[(-1)(b^2 - 4ac)]^{1/2}}{2a}$$

and can be expressed in the form of a complex conjugate as

real $\pm$ imaginary (i).

If the complex roots are not needed, a message indicating that the roots are complex can be recorded, and calculation of the roots is not required. When calculating the real roots, possible loss of significant figures as a result of subtraction of the discriminant from b can be prevented by algebraically treating the algorithm to avoid the subtraction. The loss of significant figures can be important when the discriminant value and the b value are nearly equal. A program to calculate the two real roots of a quadratic equation from given values of a, b, and c is shown below. In this program, the algorithm has been changed to prevent loss of significant digits; and when the roots are complex, an appropriate message is recorded.

```
C PROGRAM TO CALCULATE REAL ROOTS OF A QUADRATIC
          EQUATION
      READ 10, A, B, C                  or READ (5, 10)
      DISCRM = B**2 − 4.*A*C
      IF(DISCRM) 1, 2, 2
    1 PRINT 20                          or WRITE (6, 20)
      GO TO 6
    2 SRD = SQRTF(DISCRM)               or use SQRT
      IF(B) 3, 4, 4
    3 ROOT1 = (SRD − B)/(2.*A)
      ROOT2 = (2.*C)/(SRD − B)
      GO TO 5
    4 ROOT1 = −(SRD + B)/(2.*A)
      ROOT2 = −(2.*C)/(SRD + B)
    5 PRINT 30, ROOT 1, ROOT 2          or WRITE (6, 30)
   10 FORMAT(E14.7, 1XE14.7, 1XE14.7)
   20 FORMAT(13HCOMPLEX ROOTS)  or  (1Hb, 13H, etc.)
   30 FORMAT(8HROOT1 = E14.7, /, 8HROOT2 = E14.7)
          or  (1Hb, 8H, etc.)
    6 CALL EXIT
      END
```

Algorithmic relationships are available for calculating the roots of cubic and biquadratic equations, but they are fairly complex.

7-2. ITERATIVE METHODS FOR THE EVALUATION OF ROOTS.

The computer is capable of accomplishing high-speed and repetitive calculations that permit the approximation of roots of equations by numerical methods involving successive approximations. These methods are called iteration techniques. Several different methods are used for iteration, but only two will be discussed here. If a function $f(x) = 0$ can be rearranged to the form $x = g(x)$, that is, the equation is solved for x as a function of x, an approximation of a real root can be made by iteration. Iteration, which refers to a process of repeated evaluations, involves the following steps:

1. An approximation or guess of the root, called x_0, is made and is used to calculate a new approximation of the root, x_1, from the function $x = g(x)$. This step can be expressed as

$$x_1 = g(x_0).$$

2. The new approximate value is used in the function to find a hopefully better approximate x_2. Thus

$$x_2 = g(x_1).$$

3. The process is repeated again and again. Each subsequent x value is used to approximate a new x value until a good approximation of the root is obtained. A good approximation is found when the difference between subsequent values of x is within an arbitrarily established limit of accuracy. Of course, a comparison of subsequent values must be made after each iteration step, and more stringent limits of accuracy require more iteration steps. A flow chart for the iteration method is shown in Figure 7-1.

To illustrate this method, consider the determination of a root of the equation $2x - \log x - 4 = 0$. Rearrangement of this function to a form that can be used for iteration gives $x = (\log x + 4)/2$. This can be expressed as an iteration formula like $x_i = [\log(x_{i-1}) + 4]/2$. It can be seen that there is a root between $x = 2$ and $x = 3$. This conclusion is based on the fact that the left-hand side of the original function is negative with $x = 2$ and positive with $x = 3$. Therefore $x = 2.5$ can be used as an initial guess. The iteration process that approximates the root to four digits past the decimal point using the iteration formula is

$$x_1 = \frac{\log(2.5) + 4}{2} = 2.1989$$

$$x_2 = \frac{\log(2.1989) + 4}{2} = 2.1711$$

$$x_3 = \frac{\log(2.1711) + 4}{2} = 2.1680$$

$$x_4 = \frac{\log(2.1680) + 4}{2} = 2.1680.$$

Another iteration method that is quite effective is the Newton-Raphson method, which can be best explained by a graphical illustration. A plot of a function $y = f(x)$ is shown in Figure 7-2. The root of interest corresponds to the intersection of the function with the x axis. If x_0 is chosen as the first approximation of the root and a line tangent to the curve at $x_0, f(x_0)$ is drawn, the intersection of the tangent line and the x axis will give a better approximation

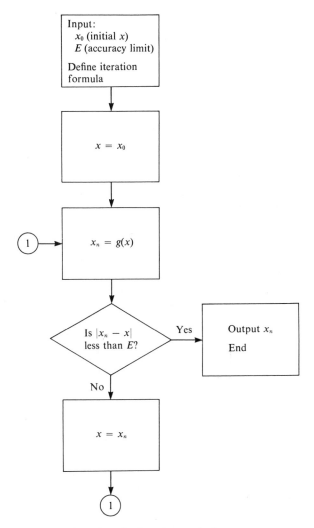

Fɪɢ. 7-1. Flow chart for iteration method.

of the root x_1. Then, if the process is repeated using the tangent line at x_1, $f(x_1)$, and so on, successively better approximations of the root will be obtained. The main problem is how to find the tangent line in each case. From purely geometrical considerations, it can be seen that the tangent will be given by

$$\tan \theta_n = \frac{f(x_n)}{x_n - x_{n+1}}.$$

As Figure 7-2 shows, the slope of the tangent line gives the slope of the curve at the point where the curve and the tangent line coincide. Thus, if the slope of the curve were known at a given point, this would provide a value for the slope

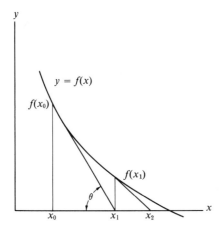

FIG. 7-2. Curve illustrating the Newton-Raphson method.

of the tangent line at that point. The slope of a curve at any point is given by the derivative of the function at that point, $f'(x_n)$. Hence a useful iteration formula can be developed using the derivative in place of the tan θ_n. Substituting $f'(x_n)$ for tan θ_n in the above formula gives

$$f'(x_n) = \frac{f(x_n)}{x_n - x_{n+1}}.$$

Solving for x_{n+1} gives the general Newton-Raphson iteration formula:

$$x_{n+1} = x_n - \frac{f(x_n)}{f'(x_n)}.$$

This iteration formula can be used in the same way as the previously discussed iteration formula. Of course, it is necessary to know the derivative of the function. The derivatives of some common functions are shown in Table 7-1. The flow chart for iteration by the Newton-Raphson method would be essentially

TABLE 7-1. Derivatives of Some Common Functions

Function $f(x)$	Derivative $f'(x)$
$y = k$ (constant)	0
$y = x^n$	nx^{n-1}
$y = e^x$	e^x
$y = \ln x$	$1/x$
$y = \sin(x)$	$\cos(x)$
$y = \cos(x)$	$-\sin(x)$
$y = ax^2 + bx + c$	$2ax + b$
$y = ax^3 + bx^2 + cx + d$	$3ax^2 + 2bx + c$
$y = ax^4 + bx^3 + cx^2 + dx + e$	$4ax^3 + 3bx^2 + 2cx + d$

the same as the flow chart in Figure 7-1, except that $x_n = g(x)$ would be replaced by the iteration formula $x_{n+1} = x_n - [f(x_n)/f'(x_n)]$.

To illustrate the Newton-Raphson method, consider the determination of a root of the equation $x^3 + x^2 + 3x + 4 = 0$. Note that a sign change occurs between $x = 0$ and $x = -2$, so at least one root is within this interval. As a first approximation for the iteration process, -1.5 can be used. For this cubic equation, the Newton-Raphson iteration formula would be

$$x_{n+1} = x_n - \frac{(x_n)^3 + (x_n)^2 + 3x_n + 4}{3(x_n)^2 + 2x_n + 3}.$$

Starting with an x_0 of -1.5, the iteration process would give the following results:

$$x_1 = -1.5 - \frac{(-1.5)^3 + (-1.5)^2 + 3(-1.5) + 4}{3(-1.5)^2 + 2(-1.5) + 3} = -1.259$$

$$x_2 = -1.259 - \frac{(-1.259)^3 + (-1.259)^2 + 3(-1.259) + 4}{3(-1.259)^2 + 2(-1.259) + 3} = -1.2232$$

$$x_3 = -1.2232 - \frac{(-1.2232)^3 + (-1.2232)^2 + 3(-1.2232) + 4}{3(-1.2232)^2 + 2(-1.2232) + 3}$$

$$= -1.222495$$

$$x_4 = -1.222495 - \frac{(-1.222495)^3 + (-1.222495)^2 + 3(-1.222495) + 4}{3(-1.222495)^2 + 2(-1.222495) + 3}$$

$$= -1.222495.$$

Some significant problems can arise when an iteration process is used to find a root of a function: the iteration formula employed may require a very large number of iterations; the iteration process may not converge on the root; or the root obtained may not be the root of interest. If successive iterations give results that are closer and closer to the root, the iteration is said to be converging. When a very large number of iterations is required, the convergence is said to be slow. This situation can be time consuming. Sometimes iteration processes do not converge on a root but diverge from it. When divergence occurs, a root is never obtained. Judicious choice of a first approximation can often avoid the problem of converging on the wrong root, but occasionally this problem occurs. However, convergence on the wrong root is usually evident. When the functions used are related to experimental or theoretical situations, a good first approximation can generally be obtained from the data or context of the problem. Frequently, the speed of convergence can be increased, or divergence can be changed to convergence, if successive approximations of the root are extrapolated to give a better approximation of the root. Many extrapolation methods are available. For example, three successive approximations, x_1, x_2, and x_3, generated in the iteration loop can be used in an extrapolation formula such as

$$x = x_3 - \frac{(x_3 - x_2)^2}{x_3 - 2x_2 + x_1}.$$

The extrapolated value, *x*, can then be used as the new approximation of the root. Such an extrapolation technique can be programmed into an iteration loop. Of course, it would require the storing of every three successive values for computation purposes. Nevertheless, the technique can be quite useful.

To avoid the problem of wasting time with slow convergence or divergence, a counter can be included in the iteration loop. The counter can be incremented and tested each time through the loop; when the counter exceeds a certain value, the iteration process can be terminated. The number of iteration attempts allowed would depend on the problem, but normally one or two hundred should be more than sufficient. The technique of using a counter in the iteration loop is included in a flow chart for the general iteration process given in Figure 7-3.

7-3. STUDENT PROGRAM 7-1.

Write a FORTRAN program to find a root of a given function by the general iteration method. The program should include the following steps:

1. Define the iteration formula in an arithmetic function statement. The formula may be a Newton-Raphson formula or some other iteration formula.

2. Input the initial guess and the desired accuracy limit. Since the initial guess can be critical, the best available guess should be used. Furthermore, the accuracy limit should be selected so that more accuracy is not required than is really needed. Very high accuracy requirements can be time consuming.

3. Initialize the counter.

4. Set *x* equal to the initial guess.

5. Set up an iteration loop using the proper iteration function. Include a counter in the loop. The loop can be controlled by IF statements that test to see if successive *x* values are within the accuracy limit and whether the number of iterations has been too great. Either of the IF statements can terminate the loop.

6. An extrapolation technique described in Section 7-2 can be added to the program to increase the chances that convergence will occur.

7. Provide a nonconverging message to be output if too many iterations are required.

8. Provide for the output of the result and accompanying description and identification.

Problems

The following problems can be solved with your basic iteration program or an altered form of the basic program. Any convenient iteration formula

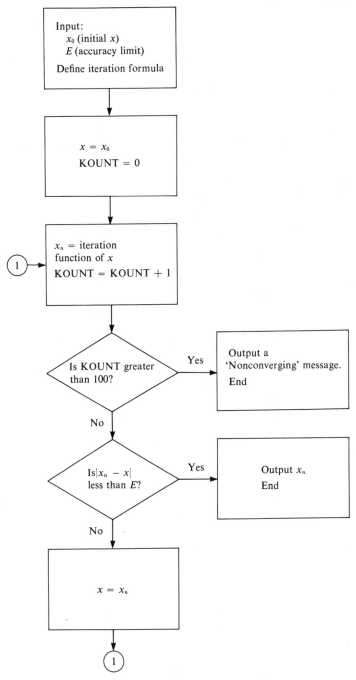

FIG. 7-3. Flow chart for the iteration method with a counter.

can be used in most of the problems. Sometimes one iteration formula will converge on a root much more quickly than another formula. The table of derivatives in Table 7-1 will be useful for the deduction of Newton-Raphson iteration formulas.

1. The Van der Waals equation of a state for a gas is

$$(P + an^2/V^2)(V - nb) = nRT.$$

P is the pressure in atmospheres, n is the number of moles, V is the volume in liters, T is the absolute temperature, and a and b are empirical constants. A list of a and b values for some gases is given in Problem 1 of Chapter 6. The equation can be rearranged to give a third-degree polynomial in terms of n.

Write a program that will read P, V, T, and a and b values from a card, along with the name of the gas. Then, using an iteration method, approximate the number of moles within an accuracy of 10^{-4}. A good first approximation of the number of moles can be obtained from the ideal gas law. Finally, output the result as well as the name of the gas.

2. Rearrange the Van der Waals equation given in Problem 1 to form a third-degree polynomial in terms of V. Then write a program to read P, T, n, and a and b values from a card, plus the name of the gas, and approximate the volume within an accuracy of 10^{-4} by an iteration process. A first guess can be obtained from the ideal gas law. Finally, output the results along with the name of the gas.

3. The equilibria that exist in an aqueous solution of a weak monoprotic acid can be described by the following relationships:

Acid equilibrium constant $\qquad K_a = \dfrac{[H_3O^+][A^-]}{[HA]}$

Ion product of water $\qquad K_w = [H_3O^+][OH^-]$
Charge balance $\qquad [H_3O^+] = [A^-] + [OH^-]$
Mass balance $\qquad C_a = [HA] + [A^-].$

C_a is the initial acid concentration in moles per liter. These relationships can be used to determine a polynomial involving $[H_3O^+]$ and K_a, K_w, and C_a; for example,

$$[H_3O^+]^3 + K_a[H_3O^+]^2 - (K_w + K_aC_a)[H_3O^+] - K_aK_w = 0.$$

Write a program to determine the pH of various aqueous solutions of a given monoprotic acid. Input the K_a, K_w, and initial C_a values from a card. The pH corresponding to the initial C_a can be determined to within an accuracy of 10^{-4} by an iteration process. A first approximation of $[H_3O^+]$ can be obtained from

$$[H_3O^+] = (C_aK_a)^{1/2}.$$

The pH can be output along with the C_a value. Then the C_a value can be decremented and the pH determined for the new C_a value, and so on, as many times as desired. Each pH determination will use the basic iteration loop; thus it must be designed appropriately. The iteration loop should be placed within a larger loop designed to carry out the decrementation process. Any convenient weak acid can be used. A concentration range of 1 M to 10^{-7} M varied in tenfold steps would be of interest.

4. For aqueous solutions of diprotic acids, the expression relating the various solution species can be used to develop a polynomial in terms of $[H_3O^+]$ and the constants. This polynomial is

$$[H_3O^+]^4 + K_1[H_3O^+]^3 + (K_1K_2 - K_w - K_1C_a)[H_3O^+]^2$$
$$- (K_1K_w + 2K_1K_2C_a)[H_3O^+] - K_1K_2K_w = 0.$$

Write a program that will read in values of K_1, K_2, and C_a from a card, and then determine the pH of the solution by solving the fourth-degree polynomial to within an accuracy of 10^{-4} via an iteration method. A first approximation can be obtained from the expression $[H_3O^+] = (C_aK_1)^{1/2}$. Finally, output the result with appropriate commentary.

5. Using the fourth-degree polynomial of Problem 4, write a program analogous to that described in Problem 3. Use any diprotic acid of interest, and decrement the concentration over the range 1 M to 10^{-7} M in tenfold steps.

6. Write a program to determine the equilibrium concentrations of all species in a solution of a given polyprotic acid. As a first step, determine the $[H_3O^+]$ of a C_a molar solution of the acid. This can be done in a manner similar to that described in Problem 4. For a triprotic or higher acid, the appropriate polynomial must be derived from the expression relating the solution species. The next step in the program will be analogous to the program described in Problem 6 of Chapter 6. That is, the $[H_3O^+]$ value can be used to determine the α_i values for the system. (See Problem 6 of Chapter 6 for a discussion of the determination of α_i values.) Finally, the α_i values can be used to determine the equilibrium concentrations of the various species in solution. This can be accomplished by the relationships

$$[H_nA] = \alpha_0C_a$$
$$[H_{n-1}A^-] = \alpha_1C_a$$
$$[H_{n-2}A^{2-}] = \alpha_2C_a$$
$$\cdot \ \cdot \ \cdot \ \cdot \ \cdot \ \cdot \ \cdot \ \cdot$$
$$[A^{n-}] = \alpha_nC_a.$$

Once the concentrations of the species are determined, they can be output along with appropriate commentary.

The program can be used to determine the concentrations of the solution species for solutions of any weak acid of any concentration. Of course, different polynomials will be involved for solutions of acids with differing numbers of protons. Consequently, the program will have to be altered for different types of acids. The program can also be used to calculate the equilibrium concentrations of species in solutions of weak bases or complex ions. In these cases, the procedure will be essentially the same. The hydronium ion concentration should be replaced by hydroxide ion concentration in the case of bases and ligand concentration in the case of complex ions. The equilibrium constants used for bases should be the basic constants, and the constants used for complex ions should be the instability constants. The C_a would correspond to the initial concentration of base in cases involving bases and to the total metal ion concentration in cases involving complex ions.

7. Write a program to determine the pH of a known volume of an aqueous solution of a weak monoprotic acid, HA, as it is titrated with a NaOH solution of known concentration. The titration of an acid, HA, with a NaOH solution involves the following relationships:

Charge balance $\qquad$ $[Na^+] + [H_3O^+] = [OH^-] + [A^-]$

Mass balance $\qquad$ $C_a = [HA] + [A^-]$

Acid constant $\qquad$ $K_a = \dfrac{[H_3O^+][A^-]}{[HA]}$

Water ion product $\qquad$ $K_w = [H_3O^+][OH^-].$

These relationships can be used to develop an expression involving only $[H_3O^+]$, $[Na^+]$, K_a, and K_w:

$$[H_3O^+]^3 + ([Na^+] + K_a)[H_3O^+]^2 + (K_a[Na^+] - K_aC_a - K_w)[H_3O^+]$$
$$- K_aK_w = 0.$$

Design the program to determine the pH to within an accuracy of 10^{-4} after the addition of each increment of C_b M NaOH solution to V_a milliliters of a C_a M acid solution. The constants, concentrations, acid volume, and base increment size can be read in from cards. The Na$^+$ concentration is changed by the volume change and is given by the expression

$$[Na^+] = (C_bV_b \text{ mmoles})/(V_a + V_b) \text{ ml}.$$

The initial pH before the addition of base can be approximated by

$$[H_3O^+] = (C_aK_1)^{1/2}.$$

Output the pH and the corresponding total volume of hydroxide solution added, V_b, after the addition of each increment of base. The size of the increment depends on the solution concentrations and volume of acid used. Be sure to choose the increment value so that the endpoint is not obscured. A plot of the pH versus the volume of NaOH solution added will give the typical titration curve.

The program can be applied to a solution of any monoprotic acid. For example, apply the program to the titration of a 50.00 ml aliquot of a 0.1000 M solution of acetic acid with a 0.1000 M solution of NaOH. It may be desirable to start with 40.00 ml of base added and then add base in increments of 1.000 ml, up to a total of 80.00 ml. This will save some calculation time. To develop the complete titration curve, however, the volume of base can be varied from 0.00 ml to 100.00 ml in increments of 1.00 ml. A similar program could be written for the titration of any polyprotic acid with a solution of a strong base or any complexometric titration. However, it would be necessary to develop the appropriate polynomials for these cases.

CHAPTER 8

NUMERICAL

INTEGRATION

8-1. THE DEFINITE INTEGRAL.

The values of definite integrals can be approximated using computer programs. The evaluation of definite integrals by numerical approximation techniques is called quadrature. Many methods have been developed for these approximations, but only three will be discussed. At this point, however, the definition of the definite integral should be described. Consider a function $y = f(x)$, defined on an interval $x = a$ and $x = b$, which is divided into n parts or subintervals by the points

$$x_0 = a, x_1, x_2, \ldots, x_{k-1}, x_k, \ldots, x_{n-1}, x_n = b.$$

Let $\Delta x_k = x_k - x_{k-1}$ and let ϵ_k be a point in the interval Δx_k. Then, consider forming the sum

$$\sum_{k=1}^{n} f(\epsilon_k) \Delta x_k.$$

Now if n is allowed to approach infinity, the Δx_k intervals approach zero and the summation approaches a limiting value, which can be expressed as

$$\lim_{n \to \infty} \sum_{k=1}^{n} f(\epsilon_k) \Delta x_k = S.$$

S is called the definite integral of the original function $f(x)$ between the limits a and b and can be denoted as

$$\int_{a}^{b} f(x) \, dx = S.$$

Most definite integrals can be evaluated using techniques of integral calculus. However, since our concern here is with the approximation of the definite integral by arithmetic, it is instructive to consider a geometrical interpretation of the definite integral. The definite integral of $f(x)$ between the limits a and b can be considered the area between the curve $y = f(x)$ and the x axis bounded by the

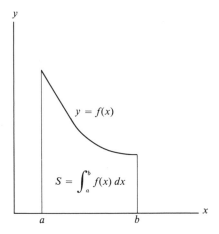

FIG. 8-1. Geometrical interpretation of the definite integral.

lines $x = a$ and $x = b$. (See Figure 8-1.) The area above the x axis is considered positive and the area below the axis, if any, is given a negative sign.

8-2. INTEGRATION BY THE TRAPEZOIDAL RULE.

Most methods of numerical approximation of these integrals involve the calculation of the area under the curve by some geometrical technique. A simple method used to approximate the area involves splitting the interval a to b into n equal subdivisions and projecting a perpendicular line from each point to the curve. Then the points of intersection of the perpendicular lines and the curve are connected with straight lines so as to form a series of trapezoidal areas, as shown in Figure 8-2. A summation of the trapezoidal areas gives an approximation of the total area under the curve bounded by a and b. The area of a trapezoid with parallel sides c and d and altitude h is

$$\tfrac{1}{2}h(c + d).$$

In terms of the notation used in the previous paragraph, the area can be expressed as

$$\tfrac{1}{2} \Delta x_k [f(x_k) + f(x_{k-1})].$$

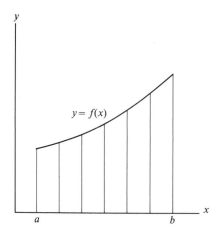

FIG. 8-2. Illustration of trapezoidal rule approximation of a definite integral.

Using this expression, the areas can be evaluated as

$$T_1 = \tfrac{1}{2}\,\Delta x_1[f(x_1) + f(a)]$$
$$T_2 = \tfrac{1}{2}\,\Delta x_2[f(x_2) + f(x_1)]$$

.   .
.   .
.   .

$$T_{n-1} = \tfrac{1}{2}\,\Delta x_{n-1}[f(x_{n-1}) + f(x_{n-2})]$$
$$T_n = \tfrac{1}{2}\,\Delta x_n[f(b) + f(x_{n-1})].$$

Since the Δx intervals are equal, the total area is given as the sum of all the trapezoidal areas.

$$T = \Delta x \left[\frac{f(a)}{2} + f(x_1) + \cdots + f(x_{n-1}) + \frac{f(b)}{2}\right]$$

In this form all the $f(x)$ or y values, with the exception of the end of the interval values, are summed; and the $f(a)/2$ and $f(b)/2$ values are added to this sum to give the total.

A FORTRAN program to calculate the total area using a known function and a given interval can easily be written. All that is required is that the values of a, b, and n or Δx are input, and the calculations using the specific function involved can be accomplished by a DO loop. A program designed for the evaluation of a definite integral using the above formula, which, incidentally, is called the trapezoidal rule, appears below.

```
C TRAPEZOIDAL RULE APPROXIMATION OF A DEFINITE INTE-
        GRAL
      THISF(X) = X**2
    2 READ 10, A, B, XN or READ (5, 10)
      DELTAX = (B − A)/XN
```

```
      FX = A + DELTAX
      N = XN
      M = N − 1
      T = 0.
      DO 20 I = 1, M
      T = T + THISF(FX)
   20 FX = FX + DELTAX
      T = (DELTAX)*(THISF(A)/2. + T + THISF(B)/2.)
      PRINT 30, A, B, N, T or WRITE (6, 30)
   10 FORMAT(E10.4, 1XE10.4, 1XE10.4)
   30 FORMAT(4HA = E10.4,1X4HB = E10.4,
              I4,1X11HINCREMENTS ,/, 11HINTEGRA
      1L = E10.4) or (1Hb, 4H, etc.)
      CALL EXIT
      END
```

Statement number 1 defines the function in an arithmetic function statement, thus eliminating the need to write the function each time it is used. Statement 2 reads in the values of *A*, *B* and the number of subdivisions. The delta *x* is calculated and a DO loop set up to sum the $f(x)$ values. The total area is then found by adding this sum to the $f(A)/2$ and $f(B)/2$ values and multiplying the result by delta *x*. Finally, the total is recorded along with appropriate commentary. Typical input and output for a given function are shown in Table 8-1. Frequently, better approximations can be obtained with larger *n* values. However, too large an *n* value will be overly time consuming.

8-3. INTEGRATION BY SIMPSON'S RULE.

The trapezoidal rule is based upon the approximation of the curve by construction of straight lines between successive pairs of points. More accurate methods of quadrature involve the approximation of the curve by passing higher-degree polynomials through the appropriate number of successive points. The higher-degree polynomials can often simulate the curve more effectively and, thus, give better results. The simplest and most useful of these methods is known as Simpson's rule, whereby a second-degree polynomial or parabolic segment is constructed through each set of three evenly spaced points. (See Figure 8-3.) It can be shown by calculus that the area under a given parabolic segment is given by

$$P_k = \frac{\Delta x}{3} [f(x_{k-1}) + 4f(x_k) + f(x_{k+1})].$$

Here the notation is the same as that used in the discussion of the trapezoidal rule. Using this expression, the formula for the Simpson's rule approximation of the area can be deduced. This formula is deduced by considering that the

TABLE 8-1. Input and Output for the Trapezoidal Rule Program

Various trapezoidal rule approximations of the definite integral of x^2 between the limits of 0 and 10. The correct answer is 333.3. Notice how a larger number of increments gives a better approximation of the integral.

1. Input
   00.0000E+0   10.0000E+0   02.0000E+1
   Output
   A = .0000E−99   B = .1000E+02   0020 INCREMENTS
   INTEGRAL = .3337E+03
2. Input
   00.0000E+0   10.0000E+0   05.0000E+1
   Output
   A = .0000E−99   B = .1000E+02   0050 INCREMENTS
   INTEGRAL = .3334E+03
3. Input
   00.0000E+0   10.0000E+0   01.0000E+2
   Output
   A = .0000E−99   B = .1000E+02   0100 INCREMENTS
   INTEGRAL = .3333E+03
4. Input
   00.0000E+0   10.0000E+0   2.0000E+2
   Output
   A = .0000E−99   B = .1000E+02   0200 INCREMENTS
   INTEGRAL = .3333E+03

total area is the summation of all of the areas under the series of parabolic segments. The formula is then

$$P = \left(\frac{2}{3}\right) \Delta x \left[\frac{f(a)}{2} + 2f(x_1) + f(x_2) + 2f(x_3) + \cdots + 2f(x_{n-1}) + \frac{f(b)}{2}\right]$$

or

$$P = \left(\frac{2}{3}\right) \Delta x \left\{\frac{f(a)}{2} + \frac{f(b)}{2} + 2[f(x_1) + f(x_3) + \cdots + f(x_{n-1})] \right.$$
$$\left. + [f(x_2) + f(x_4) + \cdots + f(x_{n-2})]\right\}.$$

Notice that the first and last terms are divided by 2 and the second and next to last are multiplied by 2. The other terms alternate between coefficients of one and two. In other words, with the exception of the first and last terms, the coefficients are two for odd terms, with respect to subscripts used above, and one for even terms. Confirm the preceding expression by using the formula for the area under a single parabolic segment given above. Note that in the Simpson's rule formula, a 2 has been factored out of each term.

   The approximation of the definite integral by Simpson's rule can easily be programmed using DO loops in a manner similar to that shown for the trapezoidal rule. Simpson's rule is one of the most widely used quadrature formulas,

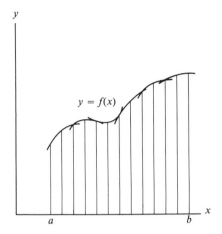

y

y = f(x)

x

a   b

FIG. 8-3. Illustration of Simpson's rule approximation of a definite integral.

especially for computer applications. When using this rule, remember that the bounding interval must be divided into an even number of parts because the method involves the construction of $n/2$ parabolic segments. Thus n must be an even number.

8-4. STUDENT PROGRAM 8-1.

Using Simpson's rule, write a FORTRAN program to approximate a definite integral. Pattern the program after the example program given for the trapezoidal rule. Among others, the program should include the following basic steps:

1. Express the function to be integrated in an arithmetic function statement.
2. Provide for card input of the a, b, and n values.
3. Set up a DO loop to accomplish the needed summations.
4. Output the results with descriptive commentary.

Keep in mind that a reasonable value for n should be used. That is, n should not be so small that a highly inaccurate result is obtained, nor should it be so large that an extremely long calculation time is required. The program can be designed to calculate three or four times, using a different n value each time. The result can be recorded for each n value and all results can be compared to obtain a measure of the effect of an increasing n. This program will be used to solve some of the problems given at the end of the chapter.

8-5. THE MONTE CARLO METHOD.

Although additional quadrature formulas are available, most are mathematically complex and require more detailed programs. One of the most important of the advanced methods, the Gaussian quadrature method, involves dividing the interval of integration into subdivisions that are not equally spaced but symmetrically spaced with respect to the middle of the interval. Another method that has become quite useful as a result of the capability of the computer to accomplish high-speed calculations is the Monte Carlo method. This method is quite simple but can be very time consuming with a relatively slow computer. In order to discuss the method, consider the problem of finding the area under the curve shown in Figure 8-4. The area under the curve is contained in the rectangular

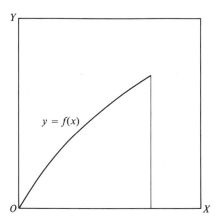

Fig. 8-4. Curve illustrating the Monte Carlo method.

area of dimensions $(X)(Y)$ as shown in the figure. The Monte Carlo method is based on the procedure of randomly selecting points, that is, sets of x and y values, within the rectangular area and then determining whether the point falls under the curve. In this way an approximation of the probability that a randomly selected point will fall under the curve can be determined. The probability of an event can be considered to be the ratio of the number of successful events to the total number of successful and unsuccessful events. Consequently, the ratio of the number of points selected that fall under the curve to the total number of points selected gives a measure of the probability of selecting a point under the curve. Smaller areas would, of course, give correspondingly lower probabilities. Once an approximation of the probability is obtained from the relationship

$$\text{Probability} = \frac{\text{Number of points under curve}}{\text{Total number of points}}$$

an approximation of the area can be found by

Area under curve = (Probability)(Total rectangular area).

The random selection of x and y values can be accomplished by a routine that serves as a random-number generator of x and y values. Subroutines that act as pseudo-random-number generators are available. An example of such a subroutine, plus explanatory notes and examples of output, appears in Table 8-2.

TABLE 8-2. Random Number Generator and an Example of the Use of the Generator

C RANDOM NUMBER GENERATOR SUBPROGRAM
* FANDK1010 (This is one type of compiler control record that controls the integer and mantissa length. Each system has a different method for controlling integer and mantissa length. See Appendix 2.)

```
      FUNCTION RNDMNM(IX)
      IX = IX*1977326743
      R = IX
      RNDMNM = R*.0000000001
      RETURN
      END
```

This subprogram can be used only if the mantissa and integer lengths are expanded to ten. (See Appendix 2.) A main program using this subprogram must also have expanded mantissa and integer lengths. The manner in which a subprogram can be linked to a main program is discussed in Appendix 3.

C MAIN PROGRAM TO ILLUSTRATE THE USE OF SUBPROGRAM
* FANDK1010

```
      TYPE 1      or WRITE (6, 1)
    1 FORMAT(15HRANDOM X VALUES, 2X15HRANDOM Y VALUES) or (1Hb,
      15H, etc.)
      DO 10 I = 1, 12
      X = RNDMNM(2)
      Y = RNDMNM(3)
      TYPE 2, X, Y     or WRITE (6, 2)
    2 FORMAT(E14.8, 3XE14.8)   or   (1Hb, E14.8, etc.)
   10 CONTINUE
      END
```

The output for this program, which uses the subprogram RNDMNM, is shown below.

RANDOM X VALUES	RANDOM Y VALUES
.39546534E−00	.59319802E−00
.71659760E−00	.57489641E−00
.82741888E−00	.24112832E−00
.85536528E−00	.78304792E−00
.57314838E−00	.85972258E−00
.48613632E−00	.72920449E−00
.65740784E−00	.48611176E−00
.85812256E−00	.28718384E−00
.55087428E−01	.58263114E−00
.77388304E−00	.16082457E−00
.32394080E−00	.48591120E−00
.75707184E−00	.63560776E−00

As a rule, random-number programs generate random numbers between zero and one. Of course, these values can be easily converted to the appropriate scale by multiplying them by the bounding dimensions of the total area (e.g., the X and Y values in Figure 8-4). Using the random-number generator, a routine that approximates the area under the curve can be devised. The routine would involve setting up a loop to obtain a set of two random numbers between 0 and 1 each time through and then converting them to an x and y value by the scale factors. The scale factors would be the sides of the rectangular area used. Then, using the value of x, the function being integrated can be evaluated for a y value. If the randomly selected y value is equal to or less than the calculated y value, the point is considered to fall under the curve and should be tallied by a counter. The total number of tries should also be tallied. After a sufficient number of tries (several thousand tries give best results), the probability can be calculated, and from this the area under the curve can be approximated.

8-6. STUDENT PROGRAM 8-2.

Using the Monte Carlo method, write a program that will approximate the definite integral of a given function over a given interval of integration. The function can be defined in an arithmetic function statement for convenience. The program can be set up according to the description above using the random number generator subroutine given or a random-number library subroutine if available.

Errors are inherent in all quadrature formulas, and care should be exercised when attempting to obtain a large number of significant digits from the calculations. Furthermore, certain functions that fluctuate widely, or are otherwise not well behaved, can make these approximation methods quite inaccurate. Fortunately, most functions involving physical situations are relatively well behaved and can be handled successfully by the quadrature methods discussed.

Problems

The following problems can be solved using your numerical integration program.

1. Test your integration program by approximating the integral of a function that can be conveniently integrated. Two possible integrals for test purposes are

$$\int_0^\pi \sin (x) \, dx = 2.0000 \text{ (Remember to use radians.)}$$

$$\int_{-1}^1 (x + 1)^2 \, dx = 2.6666.$$

2. Debye developed an expression for the theoretical calculation of the heat capacities of solids based on the vibrational frequencies of the crystal. The expression contains an integral that cannot be solved analytically. Consequently, numerical approximations of the value of the integral between appro-

priate limits is required to obtain theoretical values for heat capacities of solids. The form of the expression is

$$C_v = 9Nk \left(\frac{1}{x_0{}^3}\right) \int_0^{x_0} \frac{x^4 e^x}{(e^x - 1)^2} \, dx$$

where $x = h\nu/kT$

$x_0 = h\nu_m/kT = \theta_D/T$

$N =$ Avogadro's number $= 6.023 \times 10^{23}$

$h =$ Planck's constant $= 6.626 \times 10^{-27}$ erg sec

$k =$ Boltzman's constant $= 3.299 \times 10^{-24}$ cal deg^{-1}

$T =$ Absolute temperature

$\theta_D = h\nu_m/k$ Debye temperature

$\nu_m =$ maximum vibrational frequency. This can be determined empirically for each substance.

Some θ_D values for several elements and compounds are

Al 398	Fe 420
Na 159	KCl 227
Cu 315	NaCl 281
Ag 215	AgCl 183.

Using your Simpson's rule program, evaluate the heat capacities for one or more substances at 298 °K. Compare the calculated results to literature values. It might be necessary to alter the program somewhat to allow for the evaluation of x_0 and the multiplication of the evaluated integral by the constants to the left of the integral sign. This could be done by adding the appropriate statements before and after the DO loop evaluation of the integral, which would eliminate the need to evaluate the constant quantity each time through the DO loop. Even though zero appears as the lower limit in the integral, the function should not be evaluated with x equal to zero because e^0 equals one, which would result in division by zero when used in the function. In this case, adjusting the limits to 0.001 to x_0 should not introduce too much error.

3. Experimental observation of black-body radiation has established that the total energy emitted has an energy density (ergs cm^{-3}), which is given by

$$E(T) = 7.56 \times 10^{-15} T^4.$$

The energy flux for a black-body radiator as a function of wavelength is given by Planck's relationship:

$$E(\lambda) = \frac{8\pi hc}{\lambda^5 (e^{hc/\lambda kT} - 1)}$$

where h is Planck's constant, 6.6256×10^{-27} erg sec, c is the velocity of light, 2.99×10^{10} cm/sec, k is Boltzman's constant, 1.380×10^{-16} erg deg^{-1}, λ is the wavelength in centimeters, and T is the absolute temperature. The fraction of this total energy that is visible radiation, 4×10^{-5} cm to 7×10^{-5} cm, at a given temperature can be obtained by integrating the Planck relationship over this interval and dividing by the total energy density. This can be expressed mathematically as

$$\text{Visible fraction} = \frac{8\pi hc}{7.56 \times 10^{-15}T^4} \int_{\lambda_1}^{\lambda_2} \frac{1}{\lambda^5(e^{hc/\lambda kT} - 1)}.$$

Of course, this expression could be used to find the fraction for any wavelength interval. It may be of interest to find the fraction of infrared radiation. Furthermore, the fraction corresponding to various temperatures can be evaluated to find the effect due to a temperature change.

Approximate the fraction of visible light given off from a black-body radiator at 1500 °K by use of your Simpson's rule program. It will be necessary to alter the program so that the evaluated integral can be multiplied by the constants to the left of the integral sign. This could be accomplished by adding the appropriate statement after the DO loop evaluation of the integral. Furthermore, the temperature can be read in from a card; this would require the addition of the read and format statements. The other constants could be read in from a card or written in as part of the program.

4. Repeat Problems 1 and 2 using your Monte Carlo integration program. A few thousand random numbers can be used for the approximations. If time permits, ten thousand or more random numbers can be used. The limits a and b can be used as the x-axis boundary factors and $f(a)$ and $f(b)$ can be used as the y-axis boundary factors for integration of the function $f(x)$.

CHAPTER 9

MATRIX MANIPULATIONS

AND THE SOLUTION

OF SIMULTANEOUS

LINEAR EQUATIONS

9-1. MATRIX ALGEBRA.

Many problems in science and engineering involve the solution of simultaneous linear equations. The solution of systems of such equations can be conveniently accomplished with computer programs. For discussion purposes, consider a system of three linear equations in three unknowns:

$$a_1x_1 + b_1x_2 + c_1x_3 = k_1$$
$$a_2x_1 + b_2x_2 + c_2x_3 = k_2$$
$$a_3x_1 + b_3x_2 + c_3x_3 = k_3.$$

This system of equations can be expressed in the form of a coefficient matrix, a variable matrix, and a constant matrix:

$$\begin{bmatrix} a_1 & b_1 & c_1 \\ a_2 & b_2 & c_2 \\ a_3 & b_3 & c_3 \end{bmatrix} \begin{bmatrix} x_1 \\ x_2 \\ x_3 \end{bmatrix} = \begin{bmatrix} k_1 \\ k_2 \\ k_3 \end{bmatrix}.$$

At this point, the topic of matrices and their properties should be discussed. As mentioned earlier (see Section 2-8), a matrix is a rectangular array of numbers, the mathematical manipulation of which follows certain established rules; the members or elements of the array are generally enclosed in brackets or parentheses. Each horizontal set of elements is called a row and each vertical set is called a column. The set of elements comprising the upper-left to lower-right diagonal is called the main diagonal of the matrix. A matrix having m rows and n columns is said to be an m by n matrix. When m equals n, the matrix is an nth-order square matrix. A matrix can consist of any number of rows and columns. A matrix consisting of one column is called a column matrix, or vector. The elements of a matrix are often referred to by their row and column numbers for identification purposes. Consider, for example, the following 3 by 3 matrix:

$$A = \begin{bmatrix} a_{11} & a_{12} & a_{13} \\ a_{21} & a_{22} & a_{23} \\ a_{31} & a_{32} & a_{33} \end{bmatrix}.$$

As shown above, a given element is denoted in the subscripted form a_{ij}, where i corresponds to the row and j corresponds to the column. For example, element a_{12} of the matrix A is the element located in the first row and the second column. This type of notation permits the specific and unambiguous identification of the elements of a matrix. For simplification, a matrix can be represented by a single letter like the A above. Any set of n linearly independent equations in n unknowns can be expressed in the form of an n by n coefficient matrix, an n by 1 variable matrix, and an n by 1 constant matrix. The form in which this matrix notation for simultaneous equations is arranged was illustrated previously for a set of three simultaneous equations. In symbolic notation, the form can be expressed as

$$Ax = k.$$

Before considering methods of solving systems of equations, a brief discussion of matrix algebra will be useful. Two matrices can be added or subtracted if they have the same number of rows and columns. A new matrix C, the sum of two matrices A and B, is obtained by adding corresponding pairs of elements of A and B to form the elements of C. For example,

$$A = \begin{bmatrix} a_{11} & a_{12} \\ a_{21} & a_{22} \end{bmatrix} \qquad B = \begin{bmatrix} b_{11} & b_{12} \\ b_{21} & b_{22} \end{bmatrix}$$

$$A + B = C = \begin{bmatrix} a_{11} + b_{11} & a_{12} + b_{12} \\ a_{21} + b_{21} & a_{22} + b_{22} \end{bmatrix}.$$

This addition process can be represented as

$$c_{ij} = a_{ij} + b_{ij}.$$

Subtraction of matrices follows the same pattern except that the corresponding elements of B are subtracted from the elements of A to form the elements of C.

The product P of two matrices A and B can only be obtained if the number of columns in A is equal to the number of rows in B. Multiplication is not defined for matrices that do not meet this requirement. Each element in the product matrix P is formed from a certain arithmetic combination of the elements of A and B.

The element in the ith row and jth column of the product matrix P is found by summing the products of the successive pairs of elements of the ith row of A and the jth column of B. Expressed mathematically, for a matrix A of n columns and a matrix B of n rows, a given element of the product matrix P is

$$p_{ij} = \sum_{k=1}^{n} (a_{ik})(b_{kj}).$$

The following examples illustrate matrix multiplication:

$$\begin{bmatrix} 1 & 3 \\ 2 & 4 \end{bmatrix} \begin{bmatrix} 4 & 2 \\ -3 & 1 \end{bmatrix} = \begin{bmatrix} -5 & 5 \\ -4 & 8 \end{bmatrix}$$

$$\begin{bmatrix} 1 & 2 & -1 \\ 2 & 1 & 2 \end{bmatrix} \begin{bmatrix} 1 \\ 2 \\ 3 \end{bmatrix} = \begin{bmatrix} 2 \\ 10 \end{bmatrix}.$$

As these examples show, matrix multiplication is not commutative; that is, the product AB is not, in general, the same as the product BA. A matrix may be multiplied by a constant by multiplying each element by the constant. For example,

$$kA = k \begin{bmatrix} a_{11} & a_{12} \\ a_{21} & a_{22} \end{bmatrix} = \begin{bmatrix} ka_{11} & ka_{12} \\ ka_{21} & ka_{22} \end{bmatrix}.$$

The operation of division in the algebraic sense is not defined for matrices. However, an operation similar to division is defined for square matrices. A square matrix that has all elements of the main diagonal equal to unity and all other elements equal to zero is an identity matrix, or a unit matrix, and is represented by the symbol I. For an nth-order square matrix M, there exists a matrix denoted as M^{-1}, which when multiplied by M gives as a product an nth-order identity matrix. In matrix symbolic form, this is

$$MM^{-1} = M^{-1}M = I.$$

A matrix having the property of M^{-1} is called an inverse matrix. In this case, M^{-1} is said to be the inverse of matrix M, the parent matrix. The inverse of a given matrix can be found by the proper mathematical manipulation of the elements. The process of treating a matrix to form the inverse is called matrix inversion.

An inverse matrix can be used in the solution of a system of linear simultaneous equations. If a system of equations is represented in symbolic form as

$$Mx = k$$

the system can be solved for x by multiplying both sides of this equation by the inverse of M.

$$M^{-1}Mx = M^{-1}k$$
$$Ix = M^{-1}k$$
$$x = M^{-1}k$$

The elements of the product of the inverse matrix and the constant matrix will be the unknown x values. Note from the preceding material that the product of an identity matrix and a column matrix produces the column matrix. The process of matrix inversion and the subsequent solution of a set of simultaneous equations can be accomplished using a computer program.

9-2. SOLUTION OF LINEAR EQUATIONS BY GAUSS-JORDAN ELIMINATION.

A method similar to matrix inversion and also effective for solving a set of simultaneous equations is the Gauss-Jordan elimination method. Essentially this is the method used in elementary algebra for the same purpose. When solving a set of equations, it is valid to interchange any two equations, multiply any equation by a nonzero number, and add the product of any equation and a constant to any other equation. The elimination process involving these operations is best illustrated by an example. Suppose the system of equations is

$$5x_1 + 2x_2 + x_3 = 36$$
$$x_1 + 7x_2 + 3x_3 = 63$$
$$2x_1 + 3x_2 + 8x_3 = 81.$$

The system can be represented by a matrix of the coefficients, with an additional column containing the constants:

$$\begin{bmatrix} 5 & 2 & 1 & 36 \\ 1 & 7 & 3 & 63 \\ 2 & 3 & 8 & 81 \end{bmatrix}.$$

Such a matrix is called an augmented matrix. It can be transformed by the elimination method to give a matrix of the form

$$\begin{bmatrix} 1 & 0 & 0 & x_1 \\ 0 & 1 & 0 & x_2 \\ 0 & 0 & 1 & x_3 \end{bmatrix}.$$

Expressed in terms of the notation used in the discussion of matrix inversion, an augmented matrix formed from M and x can be changed to the augmented matrix of I and x: The values of the unknowns therefore correspond to the elements of the last column of the transformed matrix. The following steps illustrate this transformation process on the original augmented matrix given above for the system of three equations.

1. Divide the first row by the element a_{11}, which is 5 in this case.

$$\begin{bmatrix} 1 & .4 & .2 & 7.2 \\ 1 & 7 & 3 & 63 \\ 2 & 3 & 8 & 81 \end{bmatrix}$$

2. Multiply the first row by element a_{21}, which is 1, and subtract from the second row.

$$\begin{bmatrix} 1 & .4 & .2 & 7.2 \\ 0 & 6.6 & 2.8 & 55.8 \\ 2 & 3 & 8 & 81 \end{bmatrix}$$

3. Multiply the first row by element a_{31}, which is 2, and subtract from the third row.

$$\begin{bmatrix} 1 & .4 & .2 & 7.2 \\ 0 & 6.6 & 2.8 & 55.8 \\ 0 & 2.2 & 7.6 & 66.6 \end{bmatrix}$$

4. Treat the second row so that the element a_{22} is equal to one. In this case, divide by 6.6.

$$\begin{bmatrix} 1 & .4 & .2 & 7.2 \\ 0 & 1 & .425 & 8.46 \\ 0 & 2.2 & 7.6 & 66.6 \end{bmatrix}$$

5. Multiply the second row by element a_{12}, .4, and subtract from the first row; then, multiply the second row by element a_{32}, 2.2, and subtract from the third row.

$$\begin{bmatrix} 1 & 0 & .03 & 3.82 \\ 0 & 1 & .425 & 8.46 \\ 0 & 0 & 6.68 & 47.99 \end{bmatrix}$$

6. Divide the third row by 6.68 to make element a_{33} unity.

$$\begin{bmatrix} 1 & 0 & .03 & 3.82 \\ 0 & 1 & .425 & 8.46 \\ 0 & 0 & 1 & 7.19 \end{bmatrix}$$

7. Multiply the third row by element a_{13}, .03, and subtract from the first row; follow this by multiplication of the third row by element a_{23}, .425, and subtract this from the second row.

$$\begin{bmatrix} 1 & 0 & 0 & 3.6 \\ 0 & 1 & 0 & 5.4 \\ 0 & 0 & 1 & 7.2 \end{bmatrix}$$

From this last matrix, it can be seen that the values of the unknowns are

$$x_1 = 3.6, \quad x_2 = 5.4, \quad \text{and} \quad x_3 = 7.2.$$

The preceding steps follow a pattern and can be generalized. For a 3 by 3 system, the pattern is as follows:

1. Formation of the first column of the new matrix
    (a) (Row 1)/a_{11}
    (b) (Row 2) − (a_{21})(Row 1)
    (c) (Row 3) − (a_{31})(Row 1)
2. Formation of the second column of the new matrix
    (a) (Row 2)/a_{22}
    (b) (Row 1) − (a_{12})(Row 2)
    (c) (Row 3) − (a_{32})(Row 2)
3. Formation of the third column of the new matrix
    (a) (Row 3)/a_{33}
    (b) (Row 1) − (a_{13})(Row 3)
    (c) (Row 2) − (a_{23})(Row 3)

The general procedure for the kth column of the augmented matrix of $n + 1$ columns is

kth column
(Row k)/a_{kk}
(Row 1) − (a_{1k})(Row k)
(Row 2) − (a_{2k})(Row k)

.
.
.

exclude Row k

.
.
.

(Row n) − (a_{nk})(Row k).

This method, the Gauss-Jordan elimination method, will not work if any of the diagonal elements are zero. If there are no zero elements on the diagonal, no problems should arise. Often such zero elements can be avoided by prearranging the equations before the method is attempted. That is, if any of the diagonal elements are zero, the problem of division by zero can be avoided by interchanging any two rows to eliminate the zero from the diagonal. A general pattern to follow to avoid zero-diagonal elements is to interchange rows i and j if the element a_{ij} has the largest absolute value of all the elements. If the system does not have any zero-diagonal elements, then the rearrangement of rows is unnecessary.

9-3. STUDENT PROGRAM 9-1.

Write a program to solve a set of up to six simultaneous equations by the Gauss-Jordan elimination method. (A step-by-step description of the method appears in Section 9-2.) The augmented matrix of the coefficients and the constants can be read in from cards in the form of a subscripted variable. Be sure that the proper subscripts are used. Set up the necessary calculation loops needed for the elimination process. Keep in mind that it is important that none of the elements used for division be equal to zero. After the elimination method has been completed, the last column of the resulting matrix is the set of x values sought. Output these values along with an appropriate description.

9-4. SOLUTION OF SIMULTANEOUS LINEAR EQUATIONS BY MATRIX INVERSION.

We noted earlier that simultaneous equations can be solved by the matrix inversion technique. One of the best methods for matrix inversion by a computer is similar to the Gauss-Jordan elimination method. In this inversion method, an augmented matrix is formed using the coefficients and an identity matrix of the same order. For a 3 by 3 system, this augmented matrix is written

$$\begin{bmatrix} a_{11} & a_{12} & a_{13} & 1 & 0 & 0 \\ a_{21} & a_{22} & a_{23} & 0 & 1 & 0 \\ a_{31} & a_{32} & a_{33} & 0 & 0 & 1 \end{bmatrix}.$$

Here the matrix is manipulated so that the elements on the left are converted to the identity form. As a result, the elements on the right become the elements of the inverse of the coefficient matrix. In the Gauss-Jordan method, the system is represented as $Mx = k$; and the solution involves converting the augmented matrix Mk to the augmented matrix Ix. In the inversion method, the basic system is represented as $MM^{-1} = I$; and the inverse of M is found by converting the augmented matrix MI to the augmented matrix IM^{-1}. This conversion is accomplished just as in the Gauss-Jordan elimination process. That is, the steps for conversion of each column are as follows:

1. Interchange rows if needed to give nonzero diagonal elements.
2. Divide the kth row by the diagonal element of that row to give a unit diagonal element.
3. Eliminate the elements in the column of the diagonal element by proper multiplication and subtraction.

Once the inverted matrix is determined, the constant matrix can be multiplied by it to give the matrix of the unknowns. A computer program for matrix inversion would generally follow the same pattern as the Gauss-Jordan elimination method. Since a program of this type is relatively complex, a subroutine for matrix inversion is given in Figure 9-1.

Fig. 9-1   Matrix inversion subroutine

```
         SUBROUTINE MTRXIN (A, N)
         DIMENSION A(10, 10), IPV(10, 3)
C INITIALIZATION
         DO 1 J = 1, N
       1 IPV(J, 3) = 0
         DO 3 I = 1, N
C SEARCH FOR PIVOT ELEMENT
         AMAX = 0.
         DO 6 J = 1, N
         IF(IPV(J, 3) − 1) 7, 6, 7
       7 DO 6 K = 1, N
         IF(IPV(K, 3) − 1) 9, 6, 8
       9 IF(AMAX − ABSF(A(J, K))) 11, 6, 6      or use ABS
      11 IROW = J
         ICOLUM = K
         AMAX = ABSF(A(J, K))      or use ABS
       6 CONTINUE
         IPV(ICOLUM, 3) = IPV(ICOLUM, 3) + 1
         IPV(I, 1) = IROW
         IPV(I, 2) = ICOLUM
C INTERCHANGE ROWS TO PUT PIVOT ELEMENT ON DIAGONAL
         IF(IROW − ICOLUM) 16, 17, 16
      16 DO 20 L = 1, N
         SWAP = A(IROW, L)
         A(IROW, L) = A(ICOLUM, L)
      20 A(ICOLUM, L) = SWAP
C DIVIDE PIVOT ROW BY PIVOT ELEMENT
      17 PIVOT = A(ICOLUM, ICOLUM)
         A(ICOLUM, ICOLUM) = 1.0
         DO 23 L = 1, N
      23 A(ICOLUM, L) = A(ICOLUM, L)/PIVOT
C REDUCE THE NONPIVOT ROWS
         DO 3 L1 = 1, N
         IF(L1 − ICOLUM) 26, 3, 26
      26 T = A(L1, ICOLUM)
         A(L1, ICOLUM) = 0.0
         DO 29 L = 1, N
      29 A(L1, L) = A(L1, L) − A(ICOLUM, L)*T
       3 CONTINUE
C INTERCHANGE THE COLUMNS
         DO 31 I = 1, N
         L = N − I + 1
         IF(IPV(L, 1) − IPV(L, 2)) 34, 31, 34
      34 JROW = IPV(L1, 1)
         JCOLUM = IPV(L, 2)
         DO 31 K = 1, N
         SWAP = A(K, JROW)
         A(K, JROW) = A(K, JCOLUM)
         A(K, JCOLUM) = SWAP
      31 CONTINUE
      41 RETURN
         END
```

9-5. STUDENT PROGRAM 9-2.

The subroutine MTRXIN in Figure 9-1 can be used in a main program by a statement like

CALL MTRXIN(XMAT, N)

where XMAT refers to a matrix already in storage and N is the order of the matrix. Even though XMAT is a subscripted variable, it must be stated in an unsubscripted form when used as an argument in the call statement (see Section 4-3). The subroutine will invert the matrix XMAT and replace the elements of this matrix with the elements of the inverse matrix $XMAT^{-1}$.

Write a program that will read in a coefficient matrix up to 10 by 10, the corresponding constant matrix related to the system of linear simultaneous equations, and a number giving the order of the coefficient matrix. Call in the MTRXIN subroutine to invert the coefficient matrix, and then multiply the constant matrix by the inverted matrix. Finally, output the product matrix, which will consist of the values of the unknowns. The order of the unknown values may be changed if any zero-diagonal elements were encountered, so be sure to interpret the results correctly. Linkage of a subroutine with a main program is discussed in Appendix 3.

9-6. SOLUTION OF LINEAR EQUATIONS BY CRAMER'S RULE.

When working with systems of equations that are 4 by 4 or greater, either the Gauss-Jordan or the matrix inversion method is the best solution. However, the calculations required for the algebraic solution of 2 by 2 or 3 by 3 systems can easily be written into programs designed to solve such systems. For a system of two linear equations,

$$a_{11}x_1 + a_{12}x_2 = k_1$$
$$a_{21}x_1 + a_{22}x_2 = k_2$$

the algebraic solutions obtained from Cramer's rule (discussed in most college algebra courses) are

$$x_1 = \frac{a_{22}k_1 - a_{12}k_2}{a_{11}a_{22} - a_{12}a_{21}}$$

$$x_2 = \frac{a_{11}k_2 - a_{21}k_1}{a_{11}a_{22} - a_{12}a_{21}}.$$

Note that the denominators are the same in both expressions. For a system of three equations,

$$a_{11}x_1 + a_{12}x_2 + a_{13}x_3 = k_1$$
$$a_{21}x_1 + a_{22}x_2 + a_{23}x_3 = k_2$$
$$a_{31}x_1 + a_{32}x_2 + a_{33}x_3 = k_3$$

the algebraic solutions according to Cramer's rule are

$$D = a_{11}a_{22}a_{33} - a_{11}a_{23}a_{32} - a_{12}a_{21}a_{33} + a_{12}a_{23}a_{31} + a_{13}a_{21}a_{32} - a_{13}a_{22}a_{31}$$
$$x_1 = (k_1a_{22}a_{33} - k_1a_{23}a_{32} - a_{12}k_2a_{33} + a_{12}a_{23}k_3 + a_{13}k_2a_{32} - a_{13}a_{22}k_3)/D$$
$$x_2 = (a_{11}k_2a_{33} - a_{11}a_{23}k_3 - k_1a_{21}a_{33} + k_1a_{23}a_{31} + a_{13}a_{21}k_3 - a_{13}k_2a_{31})/D$$
$$x_3 = (a_{11}a_{22}k_3 - a_{11}k_2a_{32} - a_{12}a_{21}k_3 + a_{12}k_2a_{31} + k_1a_{21}a_{32} - k_1a_{22}a_{31})/D.$$

9-7. STUDENT PROGRAM 9-3.

Write a program to solve a 2 by 2 or a 3 by 3 system of linear equations, using the algebraic equations given above. The decision as to whether a 2 by 2 or a 3 by 3 system is to be treated can be made with a computed GO TO statement. The coefficients and the constants can be read in from cards in scientific notation form and stored as subscripted variables. Statements written using subscripted variables can be used for the algebraic equations. The results can be output along with any descriptive commentary desired.

9-8. SOLUTION OF NONLINEAR EQUATIONS BY ITERATION.

Sometimes, certain problems involve sets of nonlinear simultaneous equations that cannot be handled by the previous methods. In such cases, an iteration method is most satisfactory. The iteration methods are similar to those used for determining roots of equations (see Section 7-2). Consider the system of equations

$$f_1(x, y, z) = 0$$
$$f_2(x, y, z) = 0$$
$$f_3(x, y, z) = 0$$

which can be rearranged to give the following iteration formulas:

$$x_{n+1} = g_1(x_n, y_n, z_n)$$
$$y_{n+1} = g_2(x_n, y_n, z_n)$$
$$z_{n+1} = g_3(x_n, y_n, z_n).$$

With these iteration formulas, initial values of x, y, and z can be used to determine an approximate value of x. The new value of x can be used along with the other values to find an approximate value of y. The new x and y values can then be used to approximate z. Next, the process can be repeated in an iteration loop. Once each set of new values is found, it can be compared to the previous set to see if the differences are within the desired accuracy. If they are, the iteration process is terminated; if not, the process is continued. Of course, the same problems of convergence discussed in Section 7-2 arise in this iteration technique. To avoid wasting time, a check can be made on the number of iterations attempted, and the process can be terminated if convergence is too slow or if divergence is taking place. The foregoing iteration method can be extended to any number of unknowns desired. Fortunately, in many physical problems, good first approximations of the unknown values can be determined. Such approximations can often save considerable iteration time. To illustrate the iteration method, consider the system of equations involving the equilibria in an aqueous solution of a diprotic acid H_2A:

$$K_1 = \frac{[H_3O^+][HA^-]}{[H_2A]}$$

$$K_2 = \frac{[H_3O^+][A^=]}{[HA^-]}$$

$$K_w = [H_3O^+][OH^-]$$
$$[H_3O^+] = [HA^-] + 2[A^=] + [OH^-]$$
$$C_a = [H_2A] + [HA^-] + [A^=] = \text{total molar concentration of the acid.}$$

Assuming that the acid constants, the ion product of water, and C_a are known, this set of five nonlinear equations involves the five unknowns $[H_3O^+]$, $[HA^-]$, $[H_2A]$, $[A^=]$, and $[OH^-]$. However, if any two of the first four are known, the others can be determined by the first three equations. Consequently, if the equations are algebraically rearranged to give iteration formulas for $[H_3O^+]$ and $[HA^-]$, these two concentrations can be found by an iterative method.

The two iteration formulas can be deduced as follows:

$$[A^=] = \frac{[HA^-]K_2}{[H_3O^+]}$$

$$[H_2A] = \frac{[H_3O^+][HA^-]}{K_1}$$

$$C_a = \frac{[H_3O^+][HA^-]}{K_1} + [HA^-] + \frac{[HA^-]K_2}{[H_3O^+]}$$

$$C_a = [HA^-] \left\{ \frac{[H_3O^+]}{K_1} + 1 + \frac{K_2}{[H_3O^+]} \right\}$$

$$[HA^-] = \frac{C_a}{\dfrac{[H_3O^+]}{K_1} + 1 + \dfrac{K_2}{[H_3O^+]}}.$$

This is the iteration formula for $[HA^-]$. The iteration formula for $[H_3O^+]$ is obtained by making the appropriate substitutions in the charge balance:

$$[H_3O^+] = [HA^-] + \frac{2[HA^-]K_2}{[H_3O^+]} + \frac{K_w}{[H_3O^+]}.$$

Once the $[H_3O^+]$ and $[HA^-]$ have been found, the $[A^=]$ and $[H_2A]$ can be determined using the first two equations given above, and the $[OH^-]$ can be determined from the ion product of water relationship.

The application of the iteration formulas can be illustrated using a $1.0 \times 10^{-3} M$ solution of succinic acid ($K_1 = 6.2 \times 10^{-5}$ and $K_2 = 2.3 \times 10^{-6}$).

The value of 2.5×10^{-4} can be used as the initial guess for the concentrations of hydronium ion and hydrogen succinate ion. This value is obtained from $(C_a K_1)^{1/2}$. Using the initial guess for $[H_3O^+]$ in the first iteration formula given above, a new value for $[HA^-]$ can be found. This new value can be used in the second iteration equation to determine a new value for $[H_3O^+]$. The process can be repeated until sufficient approximations of the values are obtained. Even though this iteration process will converge, the rate of convergence seems to be greatly increased if the average of the former and current approximation of $[H_3O^+]$ is determined after each iteration step and used in the next iteration step. That is, the average can be found by the relationship

$$[H_3O^+]_{i+1} = \frac{[H_3O^+]_i + [H_3O^+]_{i-1}}{2}$$

and the new value can be used in the next iteration step. Using this technique, the following results are obtained:

Iteration Step	$[HA^-]$	$[H_3O^+]$
initial	2.5×10^{-4}	2.5×10^{-4}
first	1.9836×10^{-4}	2.0200×10^{-4}
second	2.1481×10^{-4}	2.1918×10^{-4}
third	2.1737×10^{-4}	2.2186×10^{-4}
fourth	2.1765×10^{-4}	2.2215×10^{-4}
fifth	2.1767×10^{-4}	2.2218×10^{-4}
sixth	2.1768×10^{-4}	2.2218×10^{-4}
seventh	2.1768×10^{-4}	2.2218×10^{-4}.

Seven iterations produce results accurate to 10^{-4}. However, remember that not all of the digits expressed are significant. The values obtained by iteration can be utilized to obtain the values of the other unknowns as shown below:

$$[A^=] = \frac{[HA^-]K_2}{[H_3O^+]} = 2.2533 \times 10^{-6}$$

$$[H_2A] = \frac{[H_3O^+][HA^-]}{K_1} = 7.8007 \times 10^{-4}$$

$$[OH^-] = \frac{K_w}{[H_3O^+]} + 4.5009 \times 10^{-11}.$$

Of course, the preceding problem could have been solved by algebraic methods that involve simplifying assumptions and was presented only as an example of the iteration method. Using a computer, the iteration method could be employed to find the equilibrium concentrations of the solution species in aqueous solutions of acids of any concentration. Furthermore, the iteration method can be used with any polyprotic acid, H_nA, solution by the general iteration formulas:

$$[H_{n-1}A^-] = C_a/([H_3O^+]/K_1 + 1 + K_2/[H_3O^+] + K_2K_3/[H_3O^+]^2 + \cdots \\ + K_2K_3 \cdots K_n/[H_3O^+]^{n-1})$$

and

$$[H_3O^+] = [H_{n-1}A^-] + (2K_2[H_{n-1}A^-])/[H_3O^+] + (3K_2K_3[H_{n-1}A^-])/[H_3O^+]^2$$
$$+ \cdots + (nK_2K_3 \cdots K_n[H_{n-1}A^-])/[H_3O^+]^{n-1} + K_w/[H_3O^+].$$

9-9. SOLUTION OF LINEAR EQUATIONS BY GAUSS-SEIDEL ITERATION.

Some systems of linear equations can be solved with an iteration technique called the Gauss-Seidel method. The basic requirement is that the absolute values of the elements of the diagonal of the coefficient matrix be large with respect to the values of the other elements. In fact, this method is especially effective when the absolute value of a given element in the diagonal is greater than the sums of the absolute values of the other elements in the row corresponding to the diagonal element. Fortunately, this requirement is often met in certain types of scientific problems, such as spectrophotometric quantitative analysis. To illustrate, consider the system of equations given below:

$$a_{11}x_1 + a_{12}x_2 + \cdots + a_{1k}x_k + \cdots + a_{1n}x_n = c_1$$
$$a_{21}x_1 + a_{22}x_2 + \cdots + a_{2k}x_k + \cdots + a_{2n}x_n = c_2$$

$$a_{k1}x_1 + a_{k2}x_2 + \cdots + a_{kk}x_k + \cdots + a_{kn}x_n = c_k$$

$$a_{n1}x_1 + a_{n2}x_2 + \cdots + a_{nk}x_k + \cdots + a_{nn}x_n = c_n.$$

For each of these equations, a formula that can be used for iteration purposes is formed by solving for the particular x value in terms of the other x values and coefficients. The iteration formulas for the above system are

$$x_1 = \frac{a_{12}x_2 + \cdots + a_{1k}x_k + \cdots + a_{1n}x_n - c_1}{(-a_{11})}$$

$$x_2 = \frac{a_{21}x_1 \quad \cdots \quad a_{2k}x_k \quad \cdots \quad a_{2n}x_n - c_2}{(-a_{22})}$$

$$x_k = \frac{a_{k1}x_1 + a_{k2}x_2 + \cdots + a_{kn}x_n - c_k}{(-a_{kk})}$$

$$x_n = \frac{a_{n1}x_1 + a_{n2}x_2 + \cdots + a_{nk}x_k + \cdots - c_n}{(-a_{nn})}.$$

To use the formulas, an initial set of x_2 through x_n values is employed to obtain a first approximation of x_1. This x_1 value, along with the other values, is used to obtain a new value for x_2. The process is continued using the new values and the needed initial values until approximate values for all the unknowns are obtained. Then the entire process is repeated in an iteration loop to produce successive sets of values for the unknowns. The iteration is continued until the differences between the set of current values of the unknowns and the previous set are small enough to satisfy the accuracy desired.

As in most iteration methods, the Gauss-Seidel method may or may not converge to give a solution. Slow convergence, which consumes an inordinate length of time, or divergence, which will not produce solutions, may occur. Whether a system converges or not depends on the system of equations and their arrangement. If the system does not meet the basic requirements previously described, problems can arise. The possibility of convergence is greater if the equations are arranged so that the a_{kk} values are as large as possible. As an example of the Gauss-Seidel method, consider the system of equations

$$5x_1 + 2x_2 + x_3 = 36$$
$$x_1 + 7x_2 + 3x_3 = 63$$
$$2x_1 + 3x_2 + 8x_3 = 81.$$

The iteration formulas that can be used for solution of this system are

$$x_1 = \frac{36 - 2x_2 - x_3}{5}, \quad x_2 = \frac{63 - x_1 - 3x_3}{7}, \quad \text{and} \quad x_3 = \frac{81 - 2x_1 - 3x_2}{8}.$$

The results of ten iteration steps starting with $x_2 = 0$ and $x_3 = 0$ are shown below.

Iteration Step	x_1	x_2	x_3
1	7.20000	7.97142	5.33571
2	2.94428	6.29265	7.02918
3	3.27710	5.51933	7.23567
4	3.54507	5.39242	7.21657
5	3.59971	5.39293	7.20271
6	3.60228	5.39850	7.19998
7	3.60059	5.39991	7.19988
8	3.60005	5.40004	7.19996
9	3.59998	5.40001	7.19999
10	3.59999	5.40000	7.20000
11	3.59999	5.40000	7.20000

9-10. STUDENT PROGRAM 9-4.

Write a program that will solve an n by n set of simultaneous equations (up to 10 by 10) by the Gauss-Seidel method. Design the program so that coefficient values are read in and stored in matrix form. The coefficients can be prearranged to enhance the convergence possibilities, or the equations can be arranged properly by the program. However, the former would reduce the programming effort. The initial values should also be read in, and an iteration loop can be set up to calculate the values of the unknowns to an accuracy of 10^{-4}. Excessive division in the iteration process can be eliminated by first dividing the coefficients corresponding to a given equation by the $-a_{kk}$ value related to that equation. This will produce a_{kk} values of unity, thus eliminating repeated division by the a_{kk} values in the iteration process. Furthermore, a count should be kept of the number of iterations so that the process can be terminated if convergence is too slow or if divergence is taking place. The loop calculations can be carried out with subscripted variables and DO loops. Finally, the results can be output along with any message desired.

Problems

The following problems can be solved by use of your simultaneous equation solving programs or some altered form of these programs.

1. According to Beer's law, the absorbance of a specific wavelength of electromagnetic radiation by a species is related to the concentration of the species by the relationship $A = \epsilon bc$, where A is the absorbance at a specific wavelength, ϵ is the absorptivity which is characteristic of the species at that wavelength, b is the thickness of the sample through which the radiation is passing, and c is the concentration of the species. If the ϵ or ϵb value can be determined experimentally from samples of known concentration, then Beer's law expression can be used in the analysis of unknown concentrations of the species involved. The absorbance of radiation by one species in solution is generally unaffected by the presence of other species. Of course, this is not true if the species interact in any way. Nevertheless, it can be stated generally that the absorbance of a solution of many species at a given wavelength is the sum of the absorbances of all the species. This can be expressed as

$$A_T = \epsilon_1 bc_1 + \epsilon_2 bc_2 + \epsilon_3 bc_3 + \cdots$$

or

$$A_T = \sum_i \epsilon_i bc_i = \sum_i k_i c_i.$$

Because of this additive characteristic of absorbances, multicomponent spectrophotometric quantitative analysis can be accomplished readily. A series of solutions of known concentrations can be used to establish the $\epsilon_i b$ values for the various components at the selected wavelengths. (See Problem 5 of Chapter 10.) Next, absorbance measurements of an unknown mixture can be made at the selected wavelengths. For an n component mixture, n wavelengths must be selected to obtain n absorbance values. The resulting set of simultaneous equations can then be solved for the concentration of each species. For example, the system of equations for a three-component system would be

$$A_1 = k_{11}c_1 + k_{12}c_2 + k_{13}c_3$$
$$A_2 = k_{21}c_1 + k_{22}c_2 + k_{23}c_3$$
$$A_3 = k_{31}c_1 + k_{32}c_2 + k_{33}c_3.$$

The matrix of the constants and the matrix of the absorbances can be used to find the concentrations.

Write a program that will read in ϵb values and absorbance values for a mixture of two or three components. The algebraic approach can then be used for the solution of the concentrations. Output the concentrations and a description.

Write another program to read ϵb values and absorbance values for up to six components. Then calculate the concentrations of each component by solving the system of equations via one of the methods previously discussed. Output the concentrations and a description.

The following spectrophotometric data can be used for calculation purposes:

(a) Analysis of an aqueous solution of Co(II) and Cr(III) ions.

	Co(II) ϵb (*l/mole*)	Cr(III) ϵb (*l/mole*)	*Unknown* Absorbances
510 mμ	5.30	6.13	0.582
585 mμ	0.631	15.19	0.485

(b) Spectrophotometric analysis of a three-component system.

	Component A ϵb (*l/mole*)	*Component B* ϵb (*l/mole*)	*Component C* ϵb (*l/mole*)	*Unknown* Absorbances
420 mμ	0.03	0.04	1.23	0.0876
540 mμ	2.05	0.06	0.63	0.1223
600 mμ	0.73	1.93	0.08	0:1380

(c) Infrared spectrophotometric analysis of a four-component system.

	p-xylene ϵb (*l/mole*)	*m-xylene* ϵb (*l/mole*)	*o-xylene* ϵb (*l/mole*)	*ethylbenzene* ϵb (*l/mole*)	*Unknown* Absorbances
12.5μ	1.502	0.0514	0	0.0408	0.1013
13.0μ	0.0261	1.1516	0	0.0820	0.09943
13.4μ	0.0342	0.0355	2.532	0.2933	0.2194
14.3μ	0.0340	0.0684	0	0.3470	0.03396

2. In mass spectrometry, a gaseous sample is subjected to an ionizing electron beam, and the resulting ions are separated by a combination of electrical and magnetic fields into the various mass to charge ratios. A mass spectrum consists of a series of peaks of varying heights that correspond to the various mass to charge ratios. The relative peak heights correspond to the relative amounts of the various ions. Furthermore, the peak heights are proportional to the pressure of the sample being used in the mass spectrograph.

Mass spectroscopy can be used for quantitative analysis of gaseous mixtures. A given component of a mixture may contribute to a given peak independently of the other components. The contributions to peak heights by the components are additive. Thus the total peak height is the sum of the contributions to that peak by the components which form the ion corresponding to the mass to charge ratio involved. For example, if two components of a mixture contribute to the height of a peak of a given mass to charge ratio, the peak height can be expressed as

$$H = r_1 s_1 p_1 + r_2 s_2 p_2.$$

where H is the height, p is the partial pressure of a component, r is the relative intensity of the ion resulting from a given component, and s is the sensitivity factor for a given component. The r values are obtained from the mass spectra of pure samples of the components of the unknown mixture that is to be analyzed. Referred to as relative intensities, these are expressed in terms of percentages of the base peak. The base peak in a mass spectrum is the highest peak in the spectrum. All peak heights can be expressed in terms of percentages of the base peak. The sensitivity factors are determined empirically from the mass spectra of the individual components. Both the r and s values are a function of the mass spectrograph being used and must be used only for mass spectrographic analysis on that specific instrument. The s is characteristic of a given component regardless of the peak involved.

Generally, for any peak, the height is given by the expression

$$H_m = r_1 s_1 p_1 + r_2 s_2 p_2 + r_3 s_3 p_3 + \cdots + r_n s_n p_n.$$

H_m is the peak height of the mth peak, p_n is the partial pressure of the nth component, r_n is the relative intensity of the nth component at the mass to charge ratio involved, and s_n is the sensitivity of the nth component. Once the r and s values have been established, analysis of an unknown mixture can be accomplished by forming a set of simultaneous equations from peak heights produced in the mass spectrum of a sample. As a rule, more peaks are available than are needed, so a choice of n equations is made for an n component mixture. Normally the appropriate peaks with the greatest H_m values are used. However, if the proper choice and arrangement of the equations are made, an iteration method of solution can be used. In the former case, a matrix of the relative intensities and a column matrix of the selected peak heights can be set up from the mass spectroscopy data. Solution of the system of equations by either approach gives the set of sp values in terms of the number of parts of the base peak of the sample. The partial pressure of each component can then be found by dividing each sp value by the appropriate sensitivity. The partial pressures of the components can next be used to calculate the mole percentages of each component using the expression

$$\text{Mole } \% = \frac{100 p_i}{\sum p_i}.$$

The results of an analysis are usually expressed in terms of mole percentages.

Write a program to read in a matrix of relative intensities, a column matrix of the corresponding peak heights, and the sensitivities for the components (up to six components). Use some routine, such as matrix inversion, to find the *sp* values. Then divide each *sp* value by the proper sensitivity values, and calculate the mole percent of each component. Finally, output the results. If the proper peaks are used for calculation purposes, a Gauss-Seidel method could be used. Otherwise one of the standard methods of solution should be applied.

Some mass spectroscopy data for mixtures are shown below. Select the best peak heights for analysis.

(a) Mass spectrographic analysis of an alcohol mixture.

Mass/Charge Ratio	Relative Intensities				Unknown Mixture
	CH_3OH	C_2H_5OH	C_3H_7OH	$(CH_3)_2CHOH$	
15	42.72	10.72	4.03	12.51	17.26
19	0.53	3.46	0.98	7.82	5.10
27	0	22.53	16.51	16.53	22.92
29	62.75	22.35	15.95	10.75	29.75
31	100.00	100.00	100.00	7.01	100.00
32	75.37	2.34	3.51	0	13.43
39		0	4.85	5.99	5.08
43		8.59	4.03	18.15	12.88
45		39.60	4.98	100.00	59.89
46		18.52	0	0	6.03
59			10.13	3.95	6.80
sensitivities	0.138	0.282	0.416	0.369	

(b) Mass spectrographic analysis of a three-component mixture.

Mass/Charge Ratio	Relative Intensities			Unknown Mixture
	A	B	C	
15	56.42	15.23	1.89	39.16
26	2.53	1.98	61.08	33.72
27	9.27	4.53	61.95	39.05
29	0.25	2.05	0.00	0.10
31	21.52	0.00	12.87	18.62
44	15.41	16.72	32.51	32.72
45	70.05	28.01	73.11	89.05
46	47.63	8.37	100.00	81.72
47	21.45	2.95	4.05	15.35
58	15.27	6.45		11.37
72	68.95	51.21		61.10
73	100.00	100.00		100.00
sensitivities	0.240	0.422	0.160	

(c) Mass spectrographic analysis of a hydrocarbon mixture.

Mass/Charge Ratio	Relative Intensities					Unknown Mixture
	n-butane	*isobutane*	*propane*	*ethane*	*methane*	
15	3.11	3.21	6.50	4.65	83.12	31.69
16	0	0	0.19	0.16	100.00	30.17
26	4.97	1.81	8.04	21.52		12.83
27	33.54	24.30	39.12	31.96		50.36
28	28.88	2.41	58.85	100.00		67.04
29	38.82	5.22	100.00	21.36		62.23
30	0.93	0	2.14	24.21		8.97
31	0	0	0	0.51		0.16
38	1.55	2.41	4.68			3.51
39	13.35	17.47	18.08			20.57
40	1.86	2.61	2.78			3.04
41	27.95	37.95	14.07			35.10
42	12.11	31.33	6.46			22.40
43	100.00	100.00	26.61			100.00
44	3.11	3.21	30.50			13.90
57	2.79	3.21				2.72
58	11.80	2.41				1.65
59	0.62	0				0.27
sensitivities	0.411	0.449	0.348	0.257	0.197	

3. Write a program to determine the concentrations of all species in a solution of a diprotic acid of a given concentration. The calculations can be made with the iteration formulas and method described in Section 9-8.

4. Write a program similar to the program described in Problem 3, but design it to find the concentrations of all species in a solution of a triprotic acid. See Section 9-8 for a theoretical discussion and the general iteration formulas.

CHAPTER 10

CURVE FITTING

10-1. LEAST-SQUARES CURVE FITTING.

In many experimental situations, a set of values for a dependent variable, which correspond to a set of selected values of the independent variable, is obtained. Once the set of y and x values is collected, it is often necessary to find a function, $v = f(x)$, that fits the set of data. The process of finding such a function is called curve fitting. A function found by the methods of curve fitting can be used to predict additional values of y. Furthermore, the constants involved in the function, such as the slope of a straight-line function, are often useful. The process of curve fitting involves fitting the best possible curve to a set of points (see Figure 10-1). By best possible curve is meant the most reasonable curve with

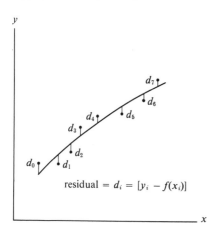

$$\text{residual} = d_i = [y_i - f(x_i)]$$

FIG. 10-1. Illustration of curve fitting.

respect to the data. That is, in an experimental situation some errors in measurement exist, and a smooth curve fitted as closely as possible to the set of points is assumed to represent the function. Often, however, the probable nature of the function is known; hence it is fitted as closely as possible to the set of points. For example, if the probable function is linear, a straight line can be fitted to the set of points.

Although several methods of curve fitting are available, only the most commonly used one will be considered here. Assuming less uncertainty in x values than in y values, each y value will deviate from the fitted curve somewhat. In other words, each experimental y value will differ from the corresponding $f(x)$ values calculated from the function and the proper x value. These deviations are called residuals and can be described as follows:

$$y_1 - f(x_1) = d_1$$
$$y_2 - f(x_2) = d_2$$
$$\cdot$$
$$\cdot$$
$$y_i - f(x_i) = d_i$$
$$\cdot$$
$$\cdot$$
$$y_n - f(x_n) = d_n.$$

When determining the best function to fit a set of points, an attempt is made to minimize these residuals. The most useful and popular method of curve fitting, the method of least squares, is based on the assumptions that the residuals will be randomly distributed and that the best representative curve for a set of data is that for which the sum of the squares of the residuals is a minimum. This sum can be expressed as

$$S = \sum_{i=1}^{n} (d_i)^2 = \sum_{i=1}^{n} [y_i - f(x_i)]^2 = \text{minimum}.$$

A curve corresponding to this minimum can be deduced from a set of data by using appropriate formulas that can be derived through differential calculus. These formulas will be given without derivation.

10-2. CURVE-FITTING POLYNOMIALS.

If we wish to fit a set of points with a polynomial of a certain degree, convenient least-squares formulas can be used. For example, consider the fitting of a set of data to a first-degree polynomial, a straight line, expressed as

$$y = b + ax.$$

For this case, two least-squares equations can be used to calculate values for *a* and *b*.

$$\sum_{i=1}^{n} y_i = nb + a \sum_{i=1}^{n} x_i$$

$$\sum_{i=1}^{n} x_i y_i = b \sum_{i=1}^{n} x_i + a \sum_{i=1}^{n} (x_i)^2$$

In these equations, the x_i and y_i values are members of a set of *n* pairs of values and *a* and *b* are the coefficients, that is, the slope and the intercept. When the summations are evaluated, these two equations form a set of simultaneous equations that can be solved to give values of *a* and *b*. Once the values of *a* and *b* are known, the function is specified. For curve fitting to any polynomial, the least-squares formulas follow a general pattern; consequently, a computer program can be written to fit a set of data to an *m*th-degree polynomial. The formulas used for an *m*th-degree polynomial comprise a set of $m + 1$ simultaneous equations that can be solved by one of the methods discussed in Chapter 9. For the general case of a polynomial

$$y_i = c_0 + c_1 x_i + c_2 (x_i)^2 + \cdots + c_k (x_i)^k + \cdots + c_m (x_i)^m$$

the least-squares formulas are

$$c_0 n + c_1 \sum x_i + c_2 \sum (x_i)^2 + \cdots + c_k \sum (x_i)^k + \cdots + c_m \sum (x_i)^m$$
$$- \sum y_i = 0$$

$$c_0 \sum x_i + c_1 \sum (x_i)^2 + c_2 \sum (x_i)^3 + \cdots + c_k \sum (x_i)^{k+1}$$
$$+ \cdots + c_m \sum (x_i)^{m+1} - \sum (x_i y_i) = 0$$

$$\cdot$$
$$\cdot$$
$$\cdot$$

$$c_0 \sum (x_i)^k + c_1 \sum (x_i)^{k+1} + c_2 \sum (x_i)^{k+2} + \cdots + c_k \sum (x_i)^{k+k}$$
$$+ \cdots + c_m \sum (x_i)^{m+k} - \sum [(x_i)^k y_i] = 0$$

$$\cdot$$
$$\cdot$$
$$\cdot$$

$$c_0 \sum (x_i)^m + c_1 \sum (x_i)^{m+1} + c_2 \sum (x_i)^{m+2} + \cdots + c_k \sum (x_i)^{m+k}$$
$$+ \cdots + c_m \sum (x_i)^{m+m} - \sum [(x_i)^m y_i] = 0.$$

In these formulas, the $\sum$ represents the summations from $i = 1$ to *n*, where *n* is the number of points being fitted. Using the general equations, show that when $m = 1$ the equations reduce to those shown previously for a straight line.

In matrix notation, the above set of general equations can be written

$$
\begin{bmatrix}
n & \sum x_i & \sum (x_i)^2 & \cdots & \sum (x_i)^k & \cdots & \sum (x_i)^m \\
\sum x_i & \sum (x_i)^2 & \sum (x_i)^3 & \cdots & \sum (x_i)^{k+1} & \cdots & \sum (x_i)^{m+1} \\
\cdot & \cdot & \cdot & & \cdot & & \cdot \\
\cdot & \cdot & \cdot & & \cdot & & \cdot \\
\cdot & \cdot & \cdot & & \cdot & & \cdot \\
\sum (x_i)^k & \sum (x_i)^{k+1} & \sum (x_i)^{k+2} & \cdots & \sum (x_i)^{k+k} & \cdots & \sum (x_i)^{m+k} \\
\cdot & \cdot & \cdot & & \cdot & & \cdot \\
\cdot & \cdot & \cdot & & \cdot & & \cdot \\
\cdot & \cdot & \cdot & & \cdot & & \cdot \\
\sum (x_i)^m & \sum (x_i)^{m+1} & \sum (x_i)^{m+2} & \cdots & \sum (x_i)^{m+k} & \cdots & \sum (x_i)^{m+m}
\end{bmatrix}
\begin{bmatrix}
c_0 \\ c_1 \\ \cdot \\ \cdot \\ \cdot \\ c_k \\ \cdot \\ \cdot \\ \cdot \\ c_m
\end{bmatrix}
=
\begin{bmatrix}
\sum y_i \\ \sum (x_i y_i) \\ \cdot \\ \cdot \\ \cdot \\ \sum [(x_i)^k y_i] \\ \cdot \\ \cdot \\ \cdot \\ \sum [(x_i)^m y_i]
\end{bmatrix}
$$

Expressing the equations like this suggests a convenient method for developing and solving them by computer. For a given m, the various summations of x can be calculated and stored in matrix (subscripted variable) form. Then the column matrix involving the other summations can be formed and stored in subscripted variable form. The inverse of the matrix involving the summations of x can next be found, and this column matrix can be multiplied by the inverse matrix to give a column matrix of the coefficients, that is, the c values. This method of solutions is discussed in Chapter 9. Alternatively, the matrix involving the summations of x and the column matrix can be used to form an augmented matrix that can be treated by the Gauss-Jordan elimination method in order to find the values of the coefficients. The elimination method is also discussed in Chapter 9.

10-3. STUDENT PROGRAM 10-1.

Write a program that will fit a set of up to 25 x and y values to a polynomial of up to the sixth degree. The desired degree of the polynomial can be read in from a card, and the points can be read in from cards in the form of subscripted variables. The various summations can then be formed by appropriate calculation loops. See Section 10-2 for the various summations needed. These summations can be stored in the form of a matrix, as shown in Section 10-2. Note that many of the elements of the matrix are identical. Thus the calculation of these sums need only be accomplished one time, and then they can be used as many times as needed to form the matrix. Once the matrix is formed, the matrix inversion routine discussed in Section 9-4 can be used to find the inverse. Next, the constant matrix can be multiplied by the inverse matrix to form a matrix of the c values of the polynomial. This matrix can then be output. Alternatively, the coefficient matrix and the constant matrix can be combined to form an augmented matrix that can be used to solve for the c values by the Gauss-Jordan elimination method discussed in Sections 9-2 and 9-3.

10-4. STRAIGHT-LINE CURVE FITTING.

Many sets of experimental data that can be fitted by a straight line, or at least should theoretically be fitted by a straight line, are collected. Consequently, straight-line curve fitting is an important case and is used frequently. The set of least-squares formulas that applies to a straight line was given previously. (See p. 156.) Using Cramer's rule, these two equations can easily be solved for the slope and the intercept. When this is done, the resulting relationships are

$$a = \frac{n \sum (y_i x_i) - \sum x_i \sum y_i}{n \sum (x_i)^2 - (\sum x_i)^2}$$

$$b = \frac{\sum (x_i)^2 \sum y_i - \sum x_i \sum (x_i y_i)}{n \sum (x_i)^2 - (\sum x_i)^2}.$$

where the summations are from $i = 1$ to n, and n is the number of points. These equations are simple enough so that once the appropriate summations are found, direct algebraic calculation of the coefficients can be carried out and the more complicated matrix method need not be used. Any set of data for which it is desirable to fit a function of the form

$$y = b + ax$$

can be used with the above expressions. Furthermore, these expressions can be applied to any function that can be manipulated so that it is in the form of the straight-line function.

If a set of data is thought to fit the function

$$y = b(e^{ax})$$

the function can be converted to a linear form by taking the logarithm of both sides, which gives

$$\ln (y) = \ln (b) + ax.$$

Of course, in this case the calculations would involve $\ln (y)$ values instead of y values and would yield a $\ln (b)$ value along with an a value. A similar case would be one in which a set of data is to be fitted to the function

$$y = bx^a.$$

This function can be converted to a linear form by using a logarithmic form; for example,

$$\ln (y) = \ln (b) + a \ln (x).$$

Here ln (y) and ln (x) values are used in the calculations, which yield an a value and a ln (b) value. Logarithmic relationships should be used with care because invalid arguments such as ln (0) can upset the calculation process.

10-5. STUDENT PROGRAM 10-2.

Write a program to calculate the a and b values, or their equivalents, for a set of x and y values that are to be fitted to a linear function. Input the x and y values from cards and store them in subscripted variable form. Then, output the slope and intercept along with a descriptive message. In some cases, it may be desirable to output the residual values, that is, the $f(x_i) - y_i$ values, so that a judgment can be made concerning how well the data fit the straight line. This option could be controlled by a computed GO TO statement.

Problems

Most of the following problems can be solved with your basic linear least-squares curve-fitting program or some altered form of it. A few will require the use of the general polynomial curve-fitting program.

1. The integrated form of the Clausius-Clapeyron equation expresses the vapor pressure of a liquid as a function of temperature. The expression is

$$\ln (p) = - \left(\frac{\Delta H_{vap}}{R} \right) \left(\frac{1}{T} \right) + K$$

where ln (p) is the natural logarithm of the vapor pressure in units of torr at the absolute temperature T, R is the gas constant, 1.9872 cal mole^{-1} deg^{-1}, and K is a constant. This expression is the equation of a straight line with a slope equal to $-(\Delta H_{vap}/R)$ and an intercept of K. Of course, ΔH_{vap} is assumed to be constant. Experimental vapor pressure data can be fitted to the straight-line relationship via your straight-line curve-fitting program. The approximate ΔH_{vap} of the liquid can be calculated by

$$\Delta H_{vap} = -(slope)R.$$

Write a program to fit vapor pressure data to the straight-line relationship given above. The ln (p) values can be calculated before the curve-fitting process, or they can be calculated as part of the DO loop calculations involving the least-squares computations. The values of vapor pressure and temperature can be read in from cards in the form of subscripted variables. Output the slope and the intercept of the resulting straight line and the ΔH_{vap} for the liquid, along with appropriate commentary. Some vapor pressure data that can be used are given on the next page.

	Vapor Pressure in torr	
Degrees Celsius	*Water*	*Chlorobenzene*
10	9.23	4.85
20	17.59	8.78
30	31.79	15.49
40	55.30	26.02
50	92.53	41.97
60	149.40	65.53
70	233.81	97.92
80	355.00	144.78
90	526.22	208.37
100	760.00	292.86

2. In kinetics, a first-order chemical reaction is a reaction in which the rate of the reaction is directly proportional to the concentration of one of the reactants. For a reaction such as $R = nP$, the rate is given by

$$\ln \left(\frac{a}{a - x} \right) = kt$$

where a is the initial concentration of the reactant, x is the amount of reactant used up at time t, and k is the specific rate constant. Kinetics data for first-order reactions such as $a/a - x$ values and corresponding t values, or $a - x$ values and corresponding t values along with an a value, can be fitted to this straight-line relationship. The slope of the line gives the rate constant k. If the stoichiometry of the reaction is known, then experimentally determined values of the amount of product, P, as a function of time can be used in the calculations. That is, x, the amount of reactant R used, will equal P/n. Of course, in such a case the a value must be known.

Write a program that will read $a/a - x$ and t values, or $a - x$ and t values along with an a value, or P and t values along with a and n values, and fit the data to the straight-line relationship given above. The calculations will differ, depending on which of the three forms of data is used. Thus a parameter indicating the case can be read in from a card and used in a computed GO TO statement to provide for branching to the proper calculations preceding the least-squares curve-fitting computations. Output the rate constant and a pertinent comment. Once the slope has been determined, it may be desirable to calculate the theoretical values of $a/a - x$ corresponding to the various t values. Using these theoretical values, the residuals can be determined by subtracting these theoretical values from the experimental values. Output of the residuals will enable the programmer to judge how well the data fit the first-order equation.

Some kinetics data for first-order reactions are given on the next page.

(a) The thermal decomposition of N_2O_5 at 44.9 °C. Partial pressure $N_2O_5 \alpha [N_2O_5]$.

Time (minutes)	Partial Pressure N_2O_5 (torr)	Time (minutes)	Partial Pressure N_2O_5 (torr)
0	348.5	70	43.4
10	248	80	32.8
20	185	90	25.3
30	142	100	19.1
40	106	120	10.5
50	79.0	140	5.12
60	56.5	160	2.99

(b) The dehydrochlorination of normal propyl chloride at 723 °K. The reaction involved is

$$CH_3CH_2CH_2Cl \rightleftharpoons CH_3CH{=}CH_2 + HCl.$$

$a/(a - x)$	Time (minutes)
1.122	4.0
1.175	5.5
1.283	7.0
1.349	9.2
1.486	12.2
1.633	14.5

(c) The hydrolysis of tertiary butyl bromide at 25 °C. a is 0.1039 M. The reaction involved is

$$(CH_3)_3CBr + 2H_2O = (CH_3)_3COH + H_3O^+ + Br^-.$$

Time (hours)	$[(CH_3)_3COH]$ (moles/l)	Time (hours)	$[(CH_3)_3COH]$ (moles/l)
0	0	18.3	0.0686
3.15	0.0143	26.0	0.0769
4.10	0.0180	30.8	0.0832
6.20	0.0263	37.3	0.0897
8.20	0.0338	43.8	0.0938
10.0	0.0400		
13.5	0.0510		

3. In a second-order chemical reaction, the rate of the reaction is proportional to the concentrations of two of the reactants. Consider the reaction $A + B = C$. Let the initial concentration of A be a and the initial concentration of B be b. After a given time t, the concentration of C will be x. The expression relating these terms to the rate constant k is

$$\frac{1}{b - a} \ln \left[\frac{a(b - x)}{b(a - x)} \right] = kt.$$

When $b = a$, the expression used is

$$\frac{x}{a(a - x)} = kt.$$

Write a program that will read in a and b values and pairs of x and t values, or pairs of $a(b - x)/b(a - x)$ values and t values, and fit the data to the linear second-order rate expression given above. Since three possible cases for the second-order expression exist, design the program to read in a parameter that can be used with a computed GO TO statement to provide for branching to the proper calculations preceding the least-squares curve-fitting computations. Once the rate constant has been found, it may be desirable to calculate the theoretical $1/(b - a) \ln [a(b - x)/b(a - x)]$ corresponding to each value of t. The residuals can then be calculated by subtracting the theoretical values from the experimental values. Output of these residuals will enable the programmer to judge how well the data fit the second-order expression.

Some kinetics data for second-order reactions are given below.

(a) The basic hydrolysis of ethyl acetate at 298 °K. The reaction involved is

$$CH_3COOC_2H_5 + OH^- = CH_3COO^- + C_2H_5OH.$$

a = initial $[OH^-]$ = $9.82 \times 10^{-3}\ M$, b = initial $[CH_3COOC_2H_5]$ = $4.84 \times 10^{-3}\ M$.

Time (sec)	$x = [C_2H_5OH]$ (moles/l)
0	0
179	8.81×10^{-4}
273	1.162×10^{-3}
530	1.862×10^{-3}
867	2.54×10^{-3}
1511	3.39×10^{-3}
1918	3.76×10^{-3}
2400	4.04×10^{-3}

(b) The reaction $(CH_3)_2CHCH_2Br + C_2H_5O^- = (CH_3)_2CHCH_2OC_2H_5 + Br^-$ at 370 °K. a = initial isobutyl bromide = $0.0507\ M$, b = initial ethoxide ion = $0.0764\ M$.

Time (sec)	x = decrease in either reactant concentration (moles/l)	Time (sec)	x = decrease in either reactant concentration (moles/l)
0	0		
152	3.00×10^{-3}	1804	2.31×10^{-2}
303	5.92×10^{-3}	2400	2.77×10^{-2}
452	8.61×10^{-3}	3002	3.12×10^{-2}
602	1.07×10^{-2}	3600	3.35×10^{-2}
783	1.36×10^{-2}	4205	3.53×10^{-2}
1022	1.68×10^{-2}	5404	3.86×10^{-2}
1205	1.80×10^{-2}	7207	4.22×10^{-2}

4. Often, in analytical chemistry, the quantitative analysis for an unknown amount of a given species is accomplished by a calibration curve, which is deter-

mined using known samples. Generally these calibration curves are linear and have the general form:

$$y = ax + b$$

where y is a measured quantity that is proportional to the amount or concentration of the species. A set of samples in which x is known can be used to obtain the corresponding y values. Then the set of x and y values can be used to establish the calibration curve. Finally, x values corresponding to experimental y values obtained in an analysis can be determined from the curve.

Write a program to read a set of y and x values obtained from known samples and then determine the slope and the intercept of the linear calibration curve by the least-squares method. Once the slope and intercept are obtained, y values obtained in analyses can be read in and the corresponding x values determined. Output the slope and intercept and any x values obtained. It may be desirable to calculate the theoretical y values related to the various x values and then calculate the residuals. (See Problem 2.) Output of the residuals will enable the programmer to judge how well the calibration curve fits a straight line. If high and/or low y values deviate greatly from linearity, the values may be deleted and the remaining values used for the calibration curve calculations. However, if the y values for the unknowns are outside the range of the known y values, the results can be quite erroneous.

Some typical data that can be used to find calibration curves are given below.

(a) In polarography, the corrected diffusion current i_d is related to the concentration c of an electrode-active species by

$$i_d = kc.$$

A calibration curve can be established by measuring the diffusion current for solutions of various concentration. The proportionality constant depends on the instrument and operating conditions. The following typical data are for an aluminum analysis:

i_d (*microamps*)	$[Al^{+3}]$ (*moles/l*)	Unknowns i_d (*microamps*)
0.207	1.23×10^{-5}	1.015
0.405	2.98×10^{-5}	0.395
0.498	3.69×10^{-5}	
0.708	5.42×10^{-5}	
0.894	7.39×10^{-5}	
1.230	9.90×10^{-5}	
1.720	1.40×10^{-4}	
2.180	1.81×10^{-4}	
2.400	2.01×10^{-4}	

(b) According to Beer's law, the absorbance A of a solution of absorbing species is proportional to the concentration of the species. The following typical data can be used to establish a calibration curve for the analysis of manganese. The absorbances refer to the absorbances of aqueous MnO_4^- solutions.

Absorbance A	mg Mn *per liter*	Absorbance A	mg Mn *per liter*
0.092	10.2	0.602	74.2
0.202	25.2	0.731	90.5
0.321	40.0	0.820	101.0
0.401	49.8	0.573	unknown
0.498	60.1	0.252	unknown

5. According to Beer's law, the absorbance A of electromagnetic radiation by a species is equal to the product of the absorptivity ϵ, the optical path length b, and the concentration of the absorbing species, c(moles per liter). This relationship can be expressed as

$$A = \epsilon bc.$$

The absorptivity at a given wavelength is characteristic for a given absorbing species. Often ϵ values or ϵb values are obtained by determining the slope of the straight line resulting from a plot of A versus bc or c. The absorbance values of several solutions of known concentration of the absorbing species are determined experimentally. From these data, the ϵ value can be determined if b is known, or the ϵb value can be determined if b is not known. For analytical purposes, the ϵb value is usually of interest.

Some instruments give percent transmittance readings rather than absorbance readings. The relationship between absorbance and percent transmittance is $A = \log(100/\%T)$. Thus Beer's law in terms of percent transmittance is $\log(100/\%T) = \epsilon bc$. Remember that this is a base ten logarithm.

Write a program to read c values and corresponding A or $\%T$ values and then determine the ϵb value by the least-squares method. The two cases can be distinguished by reading in a parameter that can be used in a computed GO TO statement to allow for branching to the proper calculations. Output the ϵb value as well as a description. It may be desirable to calculate theoretical A or $\log(100/\%T)$ values for the various c values and then calculate the residuals (see Problem 2). Output of the residuals would allow the programmer to judge how well the data fit Beer's law.

Some typical experimental values of absorbance and $\%T$ measurements are given below.

(a) Absorbance values for aqueous Cr(III) solutions at 585 mμ.

A	Cr(III) *concentration* (*moles/l*)
.745	5.00×10^{-2}
.590	4.00×10^{-2}
.438	2.98×10^{-2}
.287	1.98×10^{-2}
.137	1.01×10^{-2}

(b) Absorbance values for aqueous Co(II) solutions at 510 mμ.

A	Co(II) *concentration* (*moles/l*)
.187	3.69×10^{-2}
.385	7.40×10^{-2}
.780	1.49×10^{-1}
.990	1.88×10^{-1}

(c) Percent transmission values for MnO_4^- solutions at 540 mμ.

%T	MnO_4^- *concentration* (*moles/l*)
75.2	3.66×10^{-4}
48.1	7.30×10^{-4}
33.3	1.10×10^{-3}
21.9	1.46×10^{-3}
16.0	1.83×10^{-3}

(d) Absorbance values of solutions of ethylbenzene in cyclohexane at 14.25 microns.

A	Ethylbenzene concentration (g/100 g cyclohexane
.137	1.66×10^{-1}
.207	2.50×10^{-1}
.285	3.46×10^{-1}
.403	4.88×10^{-1}
.545	6.60×10^{-1}
.603	7.32×10^{-1}

6. Radioactive decay is a first-order process and the rate law for the disintegration can be expressed as

$$n = n_0 e^{-kt}$$

where n is the number of atoms (grams or moles) of radioactive species remaining after time t, n_0 is the initial number of atoms, and k is the radioactive decay constant characteristic of the radioactive element involved. The decay constant is related to the half-life of a radioactive species by

$$t_{1/2} = \frac{\ln 2}{k}.$$

Since radioactivity is detected by use of Geiger counters and similar counting devices, the number of counts per minute associated with a sample of a radioactive species can be considered proportional to the amount of that species. Thus the decay expression can be written

$$A = A_0 e^{-kt}$$

where A is the activity in counts per minute at time t and A_0 is the activity at zero time. The above expression can be converted to the linear form:

$$\ln A = \ln A_0 - kt.$$

Write a program that will fit experimental activities of a sample as a function of time to the preceding straight-line relationship. The activities and time values can be read in from cards and the data can be fitted by the least-squares method. Output the decay constant and the half-life along with descriptive commentary.

Some experimental values that can be used are given below.

(a) A sample of radioactive manganese gave the following activities:

Time (hr)	0	0.283	0.752	2.12	7.13	10.00	12.81	17.48
Counts/min	20,830	19,170	17,102	11,570	3130	1424	663	221

(b) A sample of a radioactive substance gave the following counting rate:

Time (min)	0	5	10	15	20	25	30	35	40	50
Counts/min	10,000	8247	6803	5610	4629	3819	3150	2600	2143	1460
Time (min)	55	60	65	70	80	85	90	100		
Counts/min	1203	993	818	675	459	378	312	257		

(c) A sample of radioactive silver gave the following counting rate:

Time (days)	0	5	10	15	20	25	30	35
Counts/min	5000	3340	2232	1492	997	666	444	297

7. Experimental molar heat capacity data often fit a power series like

$$C_p = a + bT + cT^2 + \cdots$$

where C_p is the heat capacity with units of calories deg^{-1} mole^{-1} and T is the absolute temperature. Usually the data fit the series of three terms sufficiently well, so no additional terms are needed.

Write a program to find a, b, and c corresponding to experimental values of C_p and T. Your general polynomial curve-fitting program can be used to fit the data to the quadratic. Some examples of experimental data that can be used are given below.

(a) Heat capacity data for carbon dioxide gas.

T °K	300	310	320	330	340	350	360	370	380	390	400
C_p	9.01	9.09	9.15	9.25	9.34	9.41	9.49	9.57	9.65	9.74	9.80

(b) Heat capacity data for oxygen gas.

T °K	275	280	290	300	310	320	330	340	350	360	370	390
C_p	6.93	6.94	6.96	6.70	7.03	7.05	7.07	7.10	7.13	7.14	7.17	7.19

8. Experimental specific heat measurements of water between 0 °C and 100 °C fit a power series. A graph of the data indicates that a cubic like

$$\text{sp.ht.} = a + bT + cT^2 + dT^3$$

where T is the temperature in degrees celsius, should give a good fit. Use the general polynomial curve-fitting program to fit the data below to the cubic equation.

°C	cal g^{-1} °C^{-1}	°C	cal g^{-1} °C^{-1}
0	1.00738	55	0.99895
5	1.00368	60	0.99943
10	1.00129	65	1.00000
15	0.99828	70	1.00067
20	0.99883	75	1.00143
25	0.99828	80	1.00229
30	0.99802	85	1.00327
35	0.99795	90	1.00437
40	0.99804	95	1.00561
45	0.99826	100	1.00697
50	0.99854		

9. The experimental data for the solubility of silver nitrate in water as a function of temperature are given below. Roughly plot the data to estimate the best-fitting polynomial. Then use the general polynomial curve-fitting program to find the polynomial.

T °C	Solubility (g/100 g H$_2$O)	*T* °C	Solubility (g/100 g H$_2$O)
0	113	30	271
5	135	35	300
10	160	40	333
15	185	45	366
20	214	50	400
25	240		

EIGENVALUES,

EIGENVECTORS, AND

MOLECULAR ORBITAL

CALCULATIONS

A system of linear equations often found in scientific problems has the general form, in matrix notation, of

$$Ax = \lambda x$$

where A is an nth-order square matrix with real elements, λ is a constant, and x is an unknown vector. A problem involving a system of equations such as this usually includes the determination of λ and vector x values that will satisfy the above relationship for a given matrix A. A λ that satisfies the equation is called an eigenvalue and the corresponding x is called an eigenvector. For solution purposes, the matrix equation can be rearranged as follows:

$$Ax = \lambda x$$
$$Ax - \lambda x = 0$$
$$(A - \lambda I)x = 0 \quad \text{or} \quad Ax = \lambda I x.$$

The introduction of the identity matrix I of the appropriate order is possible, for this changes the form but not the nature of the expression. To illustrate the form of the matrices in these equations, the last two of the above equations, as applied to a 4 by 4 A matrix, are

$$
\begin{bmatrix}
a_{11} - \lambda & a_{12} & a_{13} & a_{14} \\
a_{21} & a_{22} - \lambda & a_{23} & a_{24} \\
a_{31} & a_{32} & a_{33} - \lambda & a_{34} \\
a_{41} & a_{42} & a_{43} & a_{44} - \lambda
\end{bmatrix}
\begin{bmatrix}
x_1 \\ x_2 \\ x_3 \\ x_4
\end{bmatrix} = 0
$$

$$
\begin{bmatrix}
a_{11} & a_{12} & a_{13} & a_{14} \\
a_{21} & a_{22} & a_{23} & a_{24} \\
a_{31} & a_{32} & a_{33} & a_{34} \\
a_{41} & a_{42} & a_{43} & a_{44}
\end{bmatrix}
\begin{bmatrix}
x_1 \\ x_2 \\ x_3 \\ x_4
\end{bmatrix} =
\begin{bmatrix}
\lambda & 0 & 0 & 0 \\
0 & \lambda & 0 & 0 \\
0 & 0 & \lambda & 0 \\
0 & 0 & 0 & \lambda
\end{bmatrix}
\begin{bmatrix}
x_1 \\ x_2 \\ x_3 \\ x_4
\end{bmatrix}.
$$

There may be more than one eigenvalue and corresponding eigenvector for a given system. In fact, a given nth-order system will have n eigenvalues, each with a corresponding eigenvector. However, some of the eigenvalues and eigenvectors may be the same. This situation is referred to as multiplicity.

One method employed to find the eigenvalues is by determinants. The method is based on the evaluation of the expression

$$|A - \lambda I| = 0$$

where the left-hand side refers to the determinant of the matrix $A - \lambda I$. This determinant can be reduced to a polynomial, the roots of which will give the possible λ values. For an nth-order matrix, the polynomial can be expressed as

$$|A - \lambda I| = \lambda^n - c_1\lambda^{n-1} - c_2\lambda^{n-2} - \cdots - c_n = 0.$$

Once the eigenvalues are found by solving for the roots of the polynomial, the eigenvector corresponding to each eigenvalue can be obtained. For each eigenvalue, the system can be expressed as

$$B_i x_i = 0$$

where B_i is the matrix $A - \lambda I$ corresponding to a given λ value and x_i is the eigenvector associated with that value. The matrix equation given above can be evaluated for the eigenvector. This will be illustrated later, after a brief discussion of the evaluation of determinants.

A determinant is a square array of numbers to which a value can be assigned according to a definite method of evaluation. A given determinant can be considered to have a value associated with it; whereas a matrix does not have a value, even though a matrix is also an array of numbers. Determinants are denoted by enclosing the array within two parallel lines. Each vertical set of numbers constitutes a column and each horizontal set constitutes a row. Some important properties of determinants are given below without proof:

1. The value of a determinant is not changed when the columns and rows are interchanged.

2. When a row or column of a determinant is multiplied by a constant, the value of the determinant is multiplied by that constant.

3. The members of any row or column multiplied by a constant can be

added to any other row or column respectively without changing the value of the determinant.

The value of an nth-order determinant is equal to the sum of the series of products that can be formed by using only one element from each row and each column and multiplying by 1 or -1 according to a theoretically established rule. A given term in the summation has the form

$$(a_{i_1 1})(a_{i_2 2}) \cdots (a_{i_n n})$$

where i_1, $i_2 \cdots i_n$ are the row numbers in some order. The number of interchanges of subscripts of adjacent factors required to change the row subscripts in a given term, to the order $1, 2 \cdots n$ is determined. If the number of interchanges is even, the term is multiplied by 1; if it is odd, the term is multiplied by -1. For example, if the value of the determinant

$$D = \begin{vmatrix} a_{11} & a_{12} & a_{13} \\ a_{21} & a_{22} & a_{23} \\ a_{31} & a_{32} & a_{33} \end{vmatrix}$$

is desired, the method described above gives

$$D = a_{11}a_{22}a_{33} - a_{11}a_{32}a_{23} - a_{21}a_{12}a_{33} + a_{21}a_{32}a_{13} + a_{31}a_{12}a_{23} - a_{31}a_{22}a_{13}.$$

Confirm the sign of each term by applying the rule given above.

The determination of the eigenvalues and eigenvectors based on the preceding method for evaluation of a determinant can now be described. What are the eigenvalues and eigenvectors corresponding to the matrix

$$A = \begin{bmatrix} 4 & 2 \\ -1 & 1 \end{bmatrix}.$$

The solution is accomplished as follows:

$$A - \lambda I = \begin{bmatrix} 4 - \lambda & 2 \\ -1 & 1 - \lambda \end{bmatrix}$$

$$\begin{vmatrix} 4 - \lambda & 2 \\ -1 & 1 - \lambda \end{vmatrix} = (4 - \lambda)(1 - \lambda) - (-1)(2) = 0$$

$$\lambda^2 - 5\lambda + 6 = 0$$
$$(\lambda - 2)(\lambda - 3) = 0$$
$$\lambda_1 = 3, \ \lambda_2 = 2.$$

These two values are the eigenvalues that satisfy the original matrix equation. The eigenvectors can be determined from the eigenvalues as shown below.

The eigenvector corresponding to $\lambda = 3$ is found by solving the set of equations

$$\begin{bmatrix} 4 - 3 & 2 \\ -1 & 1 - 3 \end{bmatrix} \begin{bmatrix} x_1 \\ x_2 \end{bmatrix} = \begin{bmatrix} 1 & 2 \\ -1 & -2 \end{bmatrix} \begin{bmatrix} x_1 \\ x_2 \end{bmatrix} = 0.$$

For convenience in evaluation, these equations can be written

$$x_1 + 2x_2 = 0$$
$$-x_1 - 2x_2 = 0$$

from which it can be seen that the general solution gives $x_1 = -2k$ and $x_2 = k$, where k is any number. In eigenvector form, this would be

$$\begin{bmatrix} -2k \\ k \end{bmatrix}.$$

This is the general form of the eigenvector; however, it is conventional and desirable to express eigenvectors corresponding to $k = 1$. In most cases of eigenvector determination, k is considered equal to unity, which results in numerical values for the elements of the eigenvector. This notation will be used in the present discussion. Thus the above eigenvector corresponding to $\lambda = 3$ would be

$$\begin{bmatrix} -2 \\ 1 \end{bmatrix}.$$

The eigenvector corresponding to $\lambda = 2$ is found the same way; that is,

$$\begin{bmatrix} 4-2 & 2 \\ -1 & 1-2 \end{bmatrix} \begin{bmatrix} x_1 \\ x_2 \end{bmatrix} = \begin{bmatrix} 2 & 2 \\ -1 & -1 \end{bmatrix} \begin{bmatrix} x_1 \\ x_2 \end{bmatrix} = 0.$$

The equations determined from this expression are

$$2x_1 + 2x_2 = 0$$
$$-x_1 - x_2 = 0$$

from which the eigenvector

$$\begin{bmatrix} -1 \\ 1 \end{bmatrix}$$

is obtained.

The solution to the original problem can be stated as

Eigenvalue $\lambda = 3$ has the corresponding eigenvector $\begin{bmatrix} -2 \\ 1 \end{bmatrix}$

Eigenvalue $\lambda = 2$ has the corresponding eigenvector $\begin{bmatrix} -1 \\ 1 \end{bmatrix}.$

Another method of eigenvalue and eigenvector evaluation, the Jacobi method, can be conveniently programmed for computer use. Recall that the system of equations involved in an eigenvalue problem has the form

$$Ax = \lambda I x.$$

The Jacobi method is based on the transformation of matrix A to a new matrix D in which all but the diagonal elements are zero. Once the transformation has been made, it can be assumed that

$$D = \lambda I$$

and, thus, the diagonal elements of D are equal to the eigenvalues. For a 4 by 4 matrix, the process involves transforming

$$\begin{bmatrix} a_{11} & a_{12} & a_{13} & a_{14} \\ a_{21} & a_{22} & a_{23} & a_{24} \\ a_{31} & a_{32} & a_{33} & a_{34} \\ a_{41} & a_{42} & a_{43} & a_{44} \end{bmatrix}$$

into the diagonal matrix

$$\begin{bmatrix} d_{11} & 0 & 0 & 0 \\ 0 & d_{22} & 0 & 0 \\ 0 & 0 & d_{33} & 0 \\ 0 & 0 & 0 & d_{44} \end{bmatrix}.$$

The transformation process by the Jacobi method is an iterative process that is mathematically complex. The method will be discussed using matrix notation, and no detailed explanation of the actual steps will be given. From a practical point of view, the important thing to remember is that the method can be used to change an original matrix to the diagonalized form, from which the eigenvalues can be determined. The matrix A in the equation $Ax = \lambda Ix$ can be transformed to the diagonal form by manipulation of the elements, but this manipulation also effects the elements of x. The Jacobi method is based essentially on the transformation of x in such a way as to result in subsequent transformation of A to the diagonalized form. The transformation of x occurs by using a transformation relationship such as

$$x = Sx_t$$

where S is the transformation matrix and x_t is the transformed form of x. This relationship can be used as follows:

Given $\qquad\qquad\qquad\qquad Ax = \lambda x$
which can be transformed to $\qquad ASx_t = \lambda Sx_t$
and then $\qquad\qquad\qquad S'ASx_t = \lambda S'Sx_t.$

S' is the transpose of matrix S. The transpose of a given matrix is formed by interchanging the rows and columns of the matrix. In the case of the transformation matrix, the product $S'S$ is an identity matrix of the order of S. Consequently,

$$S'ASx_t = \lambda Ix_t$$
or $\qquad S'ASx_t = \lambda x_t.$

The product matrix $S'AS$ can be referred to as D and is the diagonalized form of A, if the proper S was used. The diagonal elements of D correspond to the eigenvalues. The Jacobi method therefore involves the determination of the transformation matrix S, which will produce the diagonalized form of A. Of course, the actual matrices x and x_t are not needed for solution, for only the product matrix $S'AS$ is of concern. However, once the eigenvalues are determined, the corresponding x vectors can be found.

The Jacobi method does not involve the direct determination of S; instead, D is approximated by determining various forms of S in an iteration process. In other words, an initial value of S is tried; then a new S value is determined by the proper methods, and so on, until a product matrix considered a sufficient approximation of D is found. Since an iteration process is used, this means that successive transformations are attempted until the off-diagonal elements of the product matrix are sufficiently close to zero. If n iterations are required, the diagonal matrix is given by

$$D = (S'_n) \cdots (S'_2)(S'_1)(A)(S_1)(S_2) \cdots (S_n).$$

It can be shown that an nth-order square matrix V, containing the eigenvectors as columns, can be obtained via the Jacobi method through the expression

$$V = (S_1)(S_2) \cdots (S_n).$$

In other words, a square matrix containing the approximate eigenvectors as columns is given by the product of all the transformation matrices used in the iteration process. This product can easily be determined by including such a calculation as part of the iteration loop. A given column of the matrix V is the eigenvector corresponding to the eigenvalue having the same column number in the eigenvalue matrix.

Programs using the Jacobi method are rather involved and complex. However, such a program can be very useful with certain types of problems. In chemistry the chief problems occur in Hückel linear combinations of atomic orbitals-molecular orbital calculations. A program designed basically to determine eigenvalues and eigenvectors from real symmetric matrices, but written to accommodate molecular orbital calculations, appears below (see p. 178).

Before presenting the eigenvalue program, however, a brief discussion of the molecular orbital approach seems appropriate. The molecular orbital method considers the bonding electrons in a molecule to be distributed in polynuclear orbitals associated with the molecule. The wave equation corresponding to this situation can be expressed as

$$H\psi_{\text{molecule}} = E\psi_{\text{molecule}}$$

where H is the Hamiltonian operator, ψ_{molecule} is the wave function of the molecular orbitals, and E is the energy of the molecular orbitals. In the linear combination of atomic orbitals (LCAO) approach to molecular orbital evaluation, the ψ_{molecule} is considered a linear combination of the wave functions (χ_i) of the atomic orbitals of the constituent atoms. This can be expressed as

$$\psi_{\text{molecule}} = c_1\chi_1 + c_2\chi_2 + \cdots + c_n\chi_n$$

where the c values are the weighting coefficients related to the extent of contribu-

tion of a given atomic orbital to the molecular orbital. Usually an LCAO calculation involves the determination of E in terms of the c coefficients. In this
way, the E denoting the energy of the molecular orbitals can be related to the
energies of the atomic orbitals. The coefficients can be determined by a method,
called the variation principle, in which the molecular orbital energy is considered to be a minimum, as shown by the following expression:

$$E = \frac{\int \psi H \psi \, d\tau}{\int \psi^2 \, d\tau} = \text{minimum}.$$

Here the integration is over all space and involves the space element tau, τ,
as the variable of integration. Substituting $c_1\chi_1 + c_2\chi_2 + \cdots + c_n\chi_n$ for ψ in
this expression for energy gives

$$E = \frac{\int (c_1\chi_1 + c_2\chi_2 + \cdots + c_n\chi_n)H(c_1\chi_1 + c_2\chi_2 + \cdots + c_n\chi_n) \, d\tau}{\int (c_1\chi_1 + c_2\chi_2 + \cdots + c_n\chi_n)^2 \, d\tau}$$

or upon expansion

$$E = \frac{\int (c_1\chi_1 H c_1\chi_1 + c_1\chi_1 H c_2\chi_2 + \cdots + c_1\chi_1 H c_n\chi_n + c_2\chi_2 H c_1\chi_1 + \cdots + c_2\chi_2 H c_n\chi_n + c_n\chi_n H c_1\chi_1 + \cdots + c_n\chi_n H c_n\chi_n) \, d\tau}{\int (c_1^2\chi_1^2 + 2c_1c_2\chi_1\chi_2 + c_2^2\chi_2^2 + \cdots + 2c_1c_n\chi_1\chi_n + 2c_2c_n\chi_2\chi_n + c_n^2\chi_n^2) \, d\tau}.$$

For simplification purposes, the following symbols can be used:

$$H_{ii} = \int \chi_i H \chi_i \, d\tau$$

$$H_{ij} = \int \chi_i H \chi_j \, d\tau$$

$$S_{ii} = \int \chi_i^2 \, d\tau$$

$$S_{ij} = \int \chi_i \chi_j \, d\tau.$$

Substituting these symbols into the above general expression gives

$$E = \frac{c_1^2 H_{11} + c_1 c_2 H_{12} + \cdots + c_1 c_n H_{1n} + c_1 c_2 H_{21} + c_2^2 H_{22} + \cdots + c_2 c_n H_{2n} + c_1 c_n H_{n1} + c_2 c_n H_{n2} + \cdots + c_n^2 H_{nn}}{c_1^2 S_{11} + 2c_1 c_2 S_{12} + c_2^2 S_{22} + \cdots + 2c_1 c_n S_{1n} + 2c_2 c_n S_{2n} + c_n^2 S_{nn}}.$$

Applying the variation method to this equation involves finding the partial
derivative of the equation with respect to each c_i value. This step will be omitted
here. However, application of the variation method gives the following set of
equations:

$$c_1(H_{11} - ES_{11}) + c_2(H_{12} - ES_{12}) + \cdots + c_n(H_{1n} - ES_{1n}) = 0$$
$$c_1(H_{21} - ES_{21}) + c_2(H_{22} - ES_{22}) + \cdots + c_n(H_{2n} - ES_{2n}) = 0$$

$$\cdot \qquad\qquad \cdot \qquad\qquad\qquad \cdot$$
$$\cdot \qquad\qquad \cdot \qquad\qquad\qquad \cdot$$
$$\cdot \qquad\qquad \cdot \qquad\qquad\qquad \cdot$$

$$c_1(H_{n1} - ES_{n1}) + c_2(H_{n2} - ES_{n2}) + \cdots + c_n(H_{nn} - ES_{nn}) = 0.$$

In matrix notation, these become

$$
\begin{bmatrix}
H_{11} - ES_{11} & H_{12} - ES_{12} & \cdots & H_{1n} - ES_{1n} \\
H_{21} - ES_{21} & H_{22} - ES_{22} & \cdots & H_{2n} - ES_{2n} \\
\cdot & \cdot & & \cdot \\
\cdot & \cdot & & \cdot \\
\cdot & \cdot & & \cdot \\
H_{n1} - ES_{n1} & H_{n2} - ES_{n2} & \cdots & H_{nn} - ES_{nn}
\end{bmatrix}
\begin{bmatrix}
c_1 \\ c_2 \\ \cdot \\ \cdot \\ \cdot \\ c_n
\end{bmatrix}
= 0.
$$

This set of equations can be simplified by evaluating some of the H_{ij} and S_{ij} terms. The S_{ij} integrals are sometimes referred to as the overlap integrals between atoms i and j. For the overlap integrals in which $i = j$, the S_{ij} values can be considered to be unity. That is, when $i = j$, the same atom is involved and

$$S_{ij} = S_{ii} = \int \chi_i^2 \, d\tau = 1.$$

Furthermore, for convenience of calculation all other overlap integrals can be assumed equal to zero. That is, when $i \neq j$,

$$S_{ij} = \int \chi_i \chi_j \, d\tau = 0.$$

Using these values for the overlap integrals, the system of equations can be written as

$$
\begin{bmatrix}
H_{11} - E & H_{12} & \cdots & H_{1n} \\
H_{21} & H_{22} - E & \cdots & H_{2n} \\
\cdot & \cdot & & \cdot \\
\cdot & \cdot & & \cdot \\
\cdot & \cdot & & \cdot \\
H_{n1} & H_{n2} & \cdots & H_{nn} - E
\end{bmatrix}
\begin{bmatrix}
c_1 \\ c_2 \\ \cdot \\ \cdot \\ \cdot \\ c_n
\end{bmatrix}
= 0.
$$

The H_{ij} terms are usually represented by special symbols. When $i = j$, the H_{ii} terms are called coulomb integrals and for homonuclear compounds are represented symbolically as α_i. That is, for homonuclear compounds,

$$H_{ii} = \int \chi_i H \chi_i \, d\tau = \alpha_i.$$

The other H_{ij} values are called resonance integrals and for homonuclear compounds are represented symbolically as β_{ij}. The β_{ij} values corresponding to atoms of the same type that are adjacent (bonded) are equal to β. For atoms that are not adjacent (not bonded), the β_{ij} value is assumed to be zero. In other words, for like adjacent atoms,

$$H_{ij} = \int \chi_i H \chi_j \, d\tau = \beta_{ij} = \beta$$

and for nonadjacent atoms, $\beta_{ij} = 0$. For heteronuclear compounds, the coulomb integrals for the heteroatoms and the resonance integrals between dissimilar atoms must be evaluated. Substituting the α_i and β_{ij} values into the above matrix gives

$$\begin{bmatrix} \alpha_1 - E & \beta_{12} & \cdots & \beta_{1n} \\ \beta_{21} & \alpha_2 - E & \cdots & \beta_{2n} \\ \cdot & \cdot & & \cdot \\ \cdot & \cdot & & \cdot \\ \cdot & \cdot & & \cdot \\ \beta_{n1} & \beta_{n2} & \cdots & \alpha_n - E \end{bmatrix} \begin{bmatrix} c_1 \\ c_2 \\ \cdot \\ \cdot \\ \cdot \\ c_n \end{bmatrix} = 0.$$

Note the similarity between this matrix equation and the one shown on Page 169. The system of equations represented by the above matrix has n eigenvalues, each with a corresponding eigenvector, a vector of c values. The E values represent the energies of the molecular orbitals and can be determined in terms of α and β; the c values can also be determined. Recall that these c values are the weighting coefficients of the atomic orbitals comprising the molecular orbitals. There will be one E value for each molecular orbital. Once the c values corresponding to a given E value are known, the molecular orbital wave function corresponding to that E value can be expressed in terms of the wave functions of the atomic orbitals.

To illustrate the LCAO method, consider the determination of the eigenvalues and eigenvectors for the pi bonding electrons of ozone. For notation purposes, the oxygen atoms in ozone can be labeled as follows:

0 (2)

0 (1)   0 (3).

The β_{ij} values for the nonadjacent atoms are considered zero. Thus β_{13} and β_{31} are equal to zero, while β_{12}, β_{21}, β_{23}, and β_{32} can be represented as β. Using the previously developed general matrix equation, the ozone system can be represented as

$$\begin{bmatrix} \alpha - E & \beta & 0 \\ \beta & \alpha - E & \beta \\ 0 & \beta & \alpha - E \end{bmatrix} \begin{bmatrix} c_1 \\ c_2 \\ c_3 \end{bmatrix} = 0.$$

To provide for simplified computations, the matrix of coefficients can be altered by dividing each element by β.

$$
\begin{bmatrix}
\dfrac{\alpha - E}{\beta} & 1 & 0 \\[2ex]
1 & \dfrac{\alpha - E}{\beta} & 1 \\[2ex]
0 & 1 & \dfrac{\alpha - E}{\beta}
\end{bmatrix}
\begin{bmatrix}
c_1 \\[2ex]
c_2 \\[2ex]
c_3
\end{bmatrix} = 0.
$$

This system can be solved as previously discussed. The results are

$$E_1 = \alpha - 1.414\beta \qquad \psi_1 = .5\chi_1 - .707\chi_2 + .5\chi_3$$
$$E_2 = \alpha + 1.414\beta \qquad \psi_2 = .5\chi_1 + .707\chi_2 + .5\chi_3$$
$$E_3 = \alpha \qquad\qquad\quad \psi_3 = -.707\chi_1 + .707\chi_3.$$

A general pattern that can be followed for developing the matrix equation for a given system is to use a value of one for each element of the matrix corresponding to β_{ij} values of adjacent atoms and a value of zero for each element of the matrix corresponding to β_{ij} values of nonadjacent atoms. The elements of the major diagonal will then be equal to $(\alpha - E)/\beta$, as shown in the preceding example. For compounds in which there is pi bonding, the sigma electrons can be neglected and the calculations carried out only for the pi electrons. This is the case in the above example involving ozone. Usually, in molecular orbital calculations involving unsaturated and conjugated molecules, the sigma electrons are neglected and the calculations are carried out to determine the energies of the pi molecular orbitals. For heteronuclear organic compounds involving nitrogen or oxygen, approximations of the coulomb integrals and resonance integrals in terms of α and β for carbon are available. The coulomb integral for oxygen is $\alpha + 2\beta$; the coulomb integral for nitrogen is $\alpha + \beta$. The resonance integrals are $\sqrt{2}\beta$ and β for oxygen and nitrogen, respectively.

Figure 11-1 presents a program to find the eigenvalues and eigenvectors corresponding to real symmetric matrices and to evaluate the energies and weighting coefficients for the wave functions of the molecular orbitals. The program actually determines the $(\alpha - E)/\beta$ values. For heteronuclear cases, some of the values determined by the program differ somewhat from the $(\alpha - E)/\beta$ form. However, in any case, the energies can be expressed in terms of α and β by solving for E. The program, which was written by E. R. Boyko and G. A. Whittaker of Providence College, Rhode Island, can accommodate systems of up to 12 atoms. For computers with more than 20 K storage, the program could be extended to accommodate systems with more than 12 atoms by changing the DIMENSION statement.

As can be seen from the input FORMAT statements of the program, a certain pattern must be followed for the input of data. The input of data can

Fɪɢ. 11-1. Eigenvalue and eigenvector program.

```
C PROGRAM TO COMPUTE EIGENVALUES AND EIGENVECTORS BY JACOBI
        METHOD
        DIMENSION A(12, 12), S(12, 12)
C INPUT NAME OF COMPOUND
    135 READ 7          or READ (5, 7)
C INPUT ARRAY SIZE
        READ 2, N          or READ (5, 2)
C SET EIGENVALUE MATRIX TO ZERO
C GENERATE IDENTITY MATRIX AS FIRST APPROXIMATION TO X
        DO 150 I = 1, N
        DO 150 J = 1, N
        A(I, J) = 0.0
        IF(I − J) 100, 101, 100
    100 S(I, J) = 0.0
        GO TO 150
    101 S(I, J) = 1.0
    150 CONTINUE
C SET INDICATOR WHICH CHECKS OFF-DIAGONAL ELEMENTS
        INDIC = 0
C INPUT ARRAY TO BE SOLVED
    152 READ 2, I, J, FA, IND          or READ (5, 2)
        A(I, J) = −FA
        A(J, I) = −FA
        IF (IND) 151, 152, 151
C COMPUTE INITIAL NORM
    151 VI = 0.0
        DO 106 I = 1, N
        DO 106 J = 1, N
        IF (I − J) 107, 106, 107
    107 VI = VI + A(I, J)**2
    106 CONTINUE
        VI = SQRTF(VI)          or use SQRT
C COMPUTE FINAL NORM
        VF = VI*0.1E−07
C COMPUTE THRESHOLD NORM
        AN = N
    128 VI = VI/AN
C SET UP SYSTEMATIC SEARCH
    137 IQ = 1
    124 IQ = IQ + 1
        IP = 0
    121 IP = IP + 1
        IF (A(IP, IQ)) 108, 120, 109
    108 IF (−A(IP, IQ) − VI) 120, 112, 112
    109 IF (A(IP, IQ) − VI) 120, 112, 112
    112 INDIC = 1
C COMPUTE SINE AND COSINE OF MATRIX ROTATION ANGLE
        ALAM = −A(IP, IQ)
        AMU = 0.5*(A(IP, IP) − A(IQ, IQ))
        IF (AMU) 113, 114, 114
```

```
      113  SGN = −1.0
           GO TO 115
      114  SGN = +1.0
      115  OMEGA = SGN*ALAM/SQRTF(ALAM**2 + AMU**2)          or use SQRT
           STHT = OMEGA/SQRTF(2.0 + 2.0*SQRTF(1.0 − OMEGA**2)) or use SQRT
           CTHT = SQRTF(1.0 − STHT**2)          or use SQRT
C  TRANSFORM ELEMENTS OF THE PTH AND QTH COLUMN
           DO 116 I = 1, N
           IF (I − IP) 117, 118, 117
      117  IF (I − IQ) 119, 118, 119
C  ROTATE THE SECULAR MATRIX
      119  AIPI = A(IP, I)*CTHT − A(IQ, I)*STHT
           AIQI = A(IP, I)*STHT + A(IQ, I)*CTHT
           A(IP, I) = AIPI
           A(IQ, I) = AIQI
C  ROTATE THE MATRIX  OF COEFFICIENTS
      118  AIPI = S(I, IP)*CTHT − S(I, IQ)*STHT
           AIQI = S(I, IP)*STHT + S(I, IQ)*CTHT
           S(I, IP) = AIPI
      116  S(I, IQ) = AIQI
           AIPI = A(IP, IP)*CTHT**2 + A(IQ, IQ)*STHT**2−2.*A(IP, IQ)*STHT*CTHT
           AIQI = A(IP, IP)*STHT**2 + A(IQ, IQ)*CTHT**2
                  + 2.0*A(IP, IQ)*STHT*CTHT
           AIPIQ = (A (IP, IP)−A(IQ, IQ))*CTHT*STHT
                  + A(IP, IQ)*(CTHT**2−STHT**2)
           A(IP, IP) = AIPI
           A(IQ, IQ) = AIQI
           A(IP, IQ) = AIPIQ
           A(IQ, IP) = A(IP, IQ)
C  TRANSFORM MATRIX
           DO 123 I = 1, N
           A(I, IP) = A(IP, I)
      123  A(I, IQ) = A(IQ, I)
      120  IF (IP−IQ+1) 121, 122, 122
      122  IF (IQ − N) 124, 125, 125
      125  IF (INDIC) 126, 127, 126
      126  INDIC = 0
           GO TO 137
      127  IF (VI−VF) 129, 129, 128
C  OUTPUT COMPOUND NAME
      129  TYPE 8          or WRITE (6, 8)
           TYPE 7          or WRITE (6, 7)
           TYPE 8          or WRITE (6, 8)
C  OUTPUT ROOTS TO POLYNOMIAL
           DO 130 I = 1, N
           DO 130 J = 1, N
           IF(I−J) 130, 131, 130
      131  TYPE 5, I, A(I, J)          or WRITE (6, 5)
C  OUTPUT CORRESPONDING COEFFICIENTS
           TYPE 6, J          or WRITE (6, 6)
           DO 208 IP = 1, N
      208  TYPE 3, IP, J S(IP, J)          or WRITE (6, 3)
```

(continued)

```
    130 CONTINUE
C BRANCH TO THE BEGINNING OF THE PROGRAM
        IF(IND — 99) 211, 212, 211
    212 GO TO 135
    211 CALL EXIT
C FORMAT STATEMENTS
      2 FORMAT (I5, I5, F10.4, 25X, 25X, I2)
      3 FORMAT (4X, I5, I5, E20.8)          or (1Hb, 4X etc.)
      5 FORMAT(//2X, 8HROOT NO. I3, 3H = E15.8)          or (1H0, 2X etc.)
      6 FORMAT(//2X31HCOEFFICIENTS OF WAVE FUNCTION (I3, 1H)//)
          or (1H0, 2X etc.)
      7 FORMAT(19X49H                              )  or  (1Hb, 18X etc.)
      8 FORMAT(//)  or  (1H0)
        END
```

be illustrated using the ozone problem previously discussed. First, the matrix for the system is established. For ozone, the matrix is

$$\begin{bmatrix} \dfrac{\alpha - E}{\beta} & 1 & 0 \\[2em] 1 & \dfrac{\alpha - E}{\beta} & 1 \\[2em] 0 & 1 & \dfrac{\alpha - E}{\beta} \end{bmatrix}.$$

Since the matrix is symmetrical with respect to the main diagonal, only the nonzero elements to the right of the diagonal need to be input. The program sets a_{ji} elements equal to the corresponding input a_{ij} elements. All other elements to the right and left of the main diagonal are set equal to zero by the program. Furthermore, none of the main diagonal elements need be input unless the coulomb integral is other than α. This can occur only in heteronuclear cases.

The first input card contains the name or identification of the compound involved in card columns 20 through 68. For the ozone problem, this card could be

OZONE

The second input card contains the order of the matrix (number of rows) in card columns 1 through 5 (I5 specification). For ozone, the card is

00003

The remaining cards contain the subscripts and values for all elements that must be input. One element is contained on a card according to the forms:

Row number in card columns 1 through 5 (I5 specification).
Column number in card columns 6 through 10 (I5 specifications).
Element value in card columns 11 through 20 (E10.4 specification).

The last data card should have a 99 in card columns 71 and 72 to indicate that it is the final data card. The element data cards for ozone are

Card Column 1 2 3 4 5 6 7 8 9 10 11 12 13 14 15 16 17 18 19 20 $\cdots$ 71 72

```
0 0 0 0 1 0 0 0 0 2          1 . 0 0 0 0
0 0 0 0 2 0 0 0 0 3          1 . 0 0 0 0        9 9
```

The output of the program will consist of eigenvalues, referred to as roots, and the corresponding eigenvectors, referred to as coefficients of the wave functions. Each coefficient is preceded by an integer indicating the atom and another integer indicating the eigenvalue. The atom numbering follows the same numbering pattern used to develop the original matrix. The output for the ozone problem is shown below.

OZONE

ROOT NO. 1 = .14142135E+01

COEFFICIENTS OF WAVE FUNCTION (1)

1	1	.50000005E+00
2	1	−.70710684E+00
3	1	.50000003E+00

ROOT NO. 2 = −.14142136E+01

COEFFICIENTS OF WAVE FUNCTION (2)

1	2	.50000006E+00
2	2	.70710683E+00
3	2	.50000004E+00

ROOT NO. 3 = −.27394014E−08

COEFFICIENTS OF WAVE FUNCTION (3)

1	3	−.70710682E+00
2	3	−.82012080E−08
3	3	.70710685E+00

The program is designed to accept data repeatedly and accomplish the calculations. However, if the last data card contains some nonzero integers other than 99 in card columns 71 and 72, the program will not recycle but will be terminated. Occasionally, when some of the molecular orbitals of a system are of the same energy—that is, degenerate—the calculations of the eigenvectors can be affected. This results from the iterative nature of the calculations involved in the program. The problem can be minimized by using elements that differ slightly from one another but not enough to affect the eigenvalues significantly. For example, in the benzene system, two sets of eigenvalues are degenerate; thus the input data that should be used are

Card 1	BENZENE	
Card 2	0006	
Card 3	0000100002	1.0001
Card 4	0000100006	1.0002

Card 5 0000200003	1.0003	
Card 6 0000300004	1.0004	
Card 7 0000400005	1.0005	
Card 8 0000500006	1.0006	... 89

Problems

Using the program given in Figure 11-1, determine the eigenvalues and eigenvectors for the following systems:

1. Benzene. Set up the appropriate matrix to confirm the input for benzene given above.

2. Cyclopropenone. The coulomb of oxygen is $\alpha + 2\beta$ and the carbon-oxygen resonance integral is $\sqrt{2}\beta$. This would result in one of the diagonal elements being equal to $(\alpha + 2\beta - E)/\beta$ or to $(\alpha - E)/\beta + 2$, and two of the other elements in the matrix become $\sqrt{2}$. Consequently, the diagonal element must be input as $+2$ and the other element as $\sqrt{2}$.

3. Pyrrole, C_4H_4NH. The coulomb integral for nitrogen is $\alpha + \beta$ and the nitrogen-carbon resonance integral is β. Therefore one of the diagonal elements must be input as $+1$ and the other elements must not differ from the homonuclear case.

4. Pyridine, C_5H_5N. The coulomb integral for nitrogen is $\alpha + \beta$ and the nitrogen-carbon resonance integral is β.

5. 1,3-Butadiene.

6. Naphthalene.

CHAPTER 12

MISCELLANEOUS

COMPUTER

APPLICATIONS

This chapter describes several additional problems that can be solved conveniently with appropriate computer programs. The student is encouraged to write programs to solve some of these suggested problems. In some cases, it may be desirable to consult the references for a more detailed discussion of the principles involved.

1. Prediction of Nuclear Magnetic Resonance Spectra*

The following relationships apply to the AB case of interaction between protons, in which four spectra peaks are involved:

Spacing between lines 1 and 3 and lines 2 and 4 = $(\delta^2 + J_{AB}^2)^{1/2}$
Relative intensities (peak heights) of lines 1 and 4 = $1 - [J_{AB} - (\delta^2 + J_{AB}^2)^{1/2}]$
Relative intensities (peak heights) of lines 2 and 3 = $1 + [J_{AB} - (\delta^2 + J_{AB}^2)^{1/2}]$

Write a program to predict the spacing and relative intensities for several spectra by keeping δ constant at 10 cps and varying J_{AB} from 0 to 25 cps in increments of 1 cps. Output the spacings and line intensities for each case.

For the A_2X_2, which refers to interacting nuclei with greatly differing chemical shifts, the following relationships apply:

---

* Reference: J. A. Pople, W. G. Schneider, and H. J. Bernstein, *High-Resolution Nuclear Magnetic Resonance*, McGraw-Hill Book Company, New York, 1959.

	Relative Line Positions with Respect to Center Point	Relative Line Intensities
1	$0.5N$	1
2	$0.5N$	1
3	$-0.5N$	1
4	$-0.5N$	1
5	$0.5K + 0.5(K^2 + L^2)^{1/2}$	$\sin^2 \theta_s$
6	$-0.5K + 0.5(K^2 + L^2)^{1/2}$	$\cos^2 \theta_s$
7	$0.5K - 0.5(K^2 + L^2)^{1/2}$	$\cos^2 \theta_s$
8	$-0.5K - 0.5(K^2 + L^2)^{1/2}$	$\sin^2 \theta_s$
9	$0.5M + 0.5(M^2 + L^2)^{1/2}$	$\sin^2 \theta_a$
10	$-0.5M + 0.5(M^2 + L^2)^{1/2}$	$\cos^2 \theta_a$
11	$0.5M - 0.5(M^2 + L^2)^{1/2}$	$\cos^2 \theta_a$
12	$-0.5M - 0.5(M^2 + L^2)^{1/2}$	$\sin^2 \theta_a$

$$\theta_s = 0.5 \tan^{-1}(L/K) \qquad \theta_a = 0.5 \tan^{-1}(M/K)$$
$$K = J_{AA'} + J_{XX'} \quad L = J_{AX} - J_{AX'} \quad M = J_{AA'} - J_{XX'} \quad N = J_{AX} + J_{AX'}.$$

Write a program that will input a set of J values, calculate the line positions and relative intensities, and output the results. Additional Nuclear Magnetic Resonance cases can be found in the reference or in other books covering the theoretical aspects of NMR spectra.

2. Spherical Coordinates

The expressions showing the relationships between spherical coordinates and Cartesian coordinates are

$$r = (x^2 + y^2 + z^2)^{1/2}, \quad \theta = \tan^{-1}\left[(r^2 - z^2)^{1/2}/z\right], \quad \phi = \tan^{-1}(y/x).$$

Write a subroutine that will accept a set of cartesian coordinates, and calculate the corresponding spherical coordinates.

3. Potentiometric Titrations

The endpoint in a potentiometric titration (assuming that the equivalence point is the inflection point of the titration curve) can be found by approximation of the rate of change of the potential with volume of titrant, $\Delta E/\Delta V$, and the rate of change of $\Delta E/\Delta V$ with volume of titrant. This latter rate is represented as $\Delta^2 E/\Delta V^2$. The approximation is accomplished by using a successive difference method, as shown in the following example:

	Volume of Titrant	E (or pH)	ΔE	$\Delta E/\Delta V$	$\Delta^2 E/\Delta V^2$
1	34.00	0.271			
2	34.10	0.279	.008	0.08	0.03
3	34.20	0.290	.011	0.11	0.29
4	34.30	0.330	.040	0.40	0.43
5	34.40	0.413	.083	0.83	-0.61
6	34.50	0.435	.022	0.22	-0.10
7	34.60	0.447	.012	0.12	-0.05
8	34.70	0.454	.007	0.07	

The endpoint is reached when the sign of $\Delta^2 E/\Delta V^2$ changes. Thus, in this case, the volume required to reach the endpoint is

$$V = 34.30 \text{ ml} + 0.10 \text{ ml} \left[\frac{0.43}{0.43 + 0.61} \right] = 34.34 \text{ ml}.$$

In the general case, the terms involved in the calculations are

$$\frac{\Delta E_i}{\Delta V_i} = \frac{E_{i+1} - E_i}{V_{i+1} - V_i}$$

$$\frac{\Delta^2 E_i}{\Delta V_i^2} = \frac{\Delta E_{i+1}}{\Delta V_{i+1}} - \frac{\Delta E_i}{\Delta V_i}.$$

If $\Delta^2 E_i/\Delta V_i^2$ changes sign at the ith term, then the endpoint is given by

$$V_{\text{endpoint}} = V_i + \Delta V_i \left[\frac{\Delta^2 E_{i-1}/\Delta V_{i-1}^2}{|\Delta^2 E_i/\Delta V_i^2| + \Delta^2 E_{i-1}/\Delta V_{i-1}^2} \right].$$

Write a program that will input a set of volume and voltage (or pH) values obtained from a potentiometric titration. Then, using the above approach, calculate the endpoint of the titration and output the results.

4. Prediction of Molecular Formulas from Mass Spectroscopy Data*

An algorithm for the prediction of possible molecular formulas from integer molecular weight values has been developed by Lederberg. Often mass spectroscopy data give the integer mass of a compound that has been subjected to analysis. An algorithm can be developed for any group of compounds; but only aliphatic organic compounds that contain carbon, hydrogen, oxygen, nitrogen, and, possibly, double bonds will be considered here. The formulas for such compounds can be considered to be composed of the following parts:

Terminal H	Alkane (methylene groups)	Unsaturation	Amino nitrogen	Oxygen
H	CH_2	$=$	NH	O
t	n_M	n_U	n_N	n_O

If the integer mass is divided by 14 to eliminate the possible methylene groups, the remainder must be due to some combination of the other groups. This combination must contribute a mass that, upon division by 14, equals the remainder. To determine the possible molecular formulas in terms of the groups, all that is necessary is to find linear combinations of the masses left

---

* References: J. Lederberg, *Computation of Molecular Formulas for Mass Spectroscopy*, Holden-Day, Inc., San Francisco, 1964. J. H. Benyon, *Mass Spectrometry and its Application to Organic Chemistry*, Elsevier Publishing Co., New York, 1960.

over after division by 14 which equal the remainder. This can be expressed in a formula as

$$|t - 2n_U + n_N + 2n_O| = \text{remainder left after division of integer mass by 14.}$$

Of course, in most cases there will be many valid combinations and thus many possible formulas. To deduce the actual formula, additional information is needed. As an example of the application of the algorithm, consider the integer mass 45. Division by 14 results in a quotient of 3 and a remainder of 3. Thus

$$|t - 2n_U + n_N + 2n_O| = 3.$$

The linear combinations that satisfy this relationship can be found by varying independently all the terms from 0 to 3 and checking to see which of the various combinations result in the absolute value of the above expression equaling 3. Actually, t can only take on values of 0, 1, and 2. The value of one would apply to a radical only. Consequently, it is only necessary to vary t from 0 to 2, while the other terms are varied from 0 to the value of the remainder. All combinations satisfying the relationship may correspond to possible molecular formulas. The valid combinations for the integer mass of 45 are listed below.

t	n_U	n_N	n_O	t	n_U	n_N	n_O	t	n_U	n_N	n_O
1	2	0	0	1	3	0	1	2	2	1	2
2	0	1	0	0	0	1	1	1	2	2	2
0	2	1	0	2	1	1	1	0	2	3	2
2	3	1	0	0	3	1	1	2	3	3	2
1	0	2	0	1	1	2	1	1	2	0	3
1	3	2	0	0	1	3	1	0	2	1	3
0	0	3	0	2	2	3	1	2	3	1	3
2	1	3	0	1	1	0	2	1	3	2	3
0	3	3	0	0	1	1	2	0	3	3	3
1	0	0	1								

For each of the valid combinations, the possible formulas can be deduced as follows:

The number of combined oxygen atoms and combined nitrogen atoms are given by the values of n_O and n_N, respectively. The number of carbon atoms, n_C, can be obtained by subtracting the sum of the n_O and n_N values from the quotient obtained by dividing the original mass by 14. That is, $n_C = \text{quotient} - n_O - n_N$. If n_C is negative, there is no possible formula. The number of hydrogens, n_H, can then be found using the relationship $n_H = \text{integer mass} - 12n_C - 14n_N - 16n_O$. However, complications arise when oxygen or nitrogen is not present but double bonds are. The complications result from the fact that double bonds can effect the non-CH_2 part of the mass and result in erroneous predictions. In such cases, the number of carbons is given by $n_C = (\text{integer mass} - 2n_U - t)/12$ (integer arithmetic). This is only valid when a whole number results. Hence, if $n_C - (\text{integer mass} - 2n_U - t)/12$ (arithmetic using real and not integer numbers) is not equal to zero, numerous double bonds are indicated, and the number of carbons is usually given by the relationship n_C = quotient + 1. The number of hydrogens is n_H = integer mass − $12n_C$. Of course, when the number of carbons or hydrogens is negative, no possible formula exists. Such cases should be discarded. Furthermore, two or more valid combinations may result in the same predicted formula. For the case of an integer mass of 45, the possible formulas corresponding to valid combinations are listed below:

Combination				Formula	Combination				Formula
t	n_U	n_N	n_O		t	n_U	n_N	n_O	
2	0	1	0	C_2H_7N	0	3	3	0	N_3H_3
0	2	1	0	C_2H_7N	1	0	0	1	C_2H_5O
2	3	1	0	C_2H_7N	1	3	0	1	C_2H_5O
1	0	2	0	CH_5N_2	0	0	1	1	CH_3NO
1	3	2	0	CH_5N_2	2	1	1	1	CH_3NO
0	0	3	0	N_3H_3	0	3	1	1	CH_3NO
2	1	3	0	N_3H_3	1	1	2	1	HN_2O
					1	1	0	2	CHO_2

Write a program that will input an integer mass, and then deduce the possible molecular formulas according to the pattern discussed above. Integer arithmetic can be used for most of the calculations. The number of atoms of each type can be output for each combination that gives a valid formula.

The above problem involved the prediction of possible molecular formulas from integer mass values. Selection of the best of these possible formulas can be aided by the consideration of the relative abundances of the naturally occurring isotopes of the elements in the compound. The presence of more massive isotopes of the elements in the compound can give rise to small peaks in the mass spectrum at mass to charge ratios of 1 and 2 or more units above the peak due to the ion of the parent molecule. (See Problem 2 or Chapter 9 for a discussion of mass spectrometry.) The parent ion peak (P_M) is almost always the peak of highest mass to charge ratio of significance in the mass spectrum of the compound. However, this parent peak is followed by smaller peaks (P_{M+1}, P_{M+2}, etc.) due to the contribution of the more massive isotopes. The heights of the P_{M+1} and the P_{M+2} peaks relative to the height of the P_M peak depend on the number of atoms of each type in the molecule and on the relative abundances of the more massive isotopes of these atoms. Consequently, the relative heights of these peaks depend on the molecular formula of the compound. In fact, the approximate heights of these peaks as percentages of the parent peak can be predicted for a given molecular formula. For compounds corresponding to the general formula $C_wH_xN_yO_z$, the following expressions can be used to approximate the relative peak heights:

$$P_{M+1} \text{ as a \% of } P_M \cong 1.5 \times 10^{-2}x + 1.11w + 3.7 \times 10^{-1}y + 3.7 \times 10^{-2}z$$
$$P_{M+2} \text{ as a \% of } P_M \cong 2.0 \times 10^{-1}z + 6.0 \times 10^{-3}w(w - 1) + 4.0 \times 10^{-3}wy + 2.0 \times 10^{-4}wx.$$

Write a program to input sets of w, x, y, and z values, calculate the relative peak heights, and output the results. This program could be combined with the previous one so that the relative peak heights for each possible formula could be calculated and output along with the formula. Listed below are some integer masses, plus the relative P_{M+1} and P_{M+2} peak heights obtained from mass spectra. Using the above programs, see if you can determine the actual formulas for the compounds.

Integer Mass	P_{M+1}	P_{M+2}	Answer
60	2.30	0.0416	$C_2H_4O_2$
103	4.93	0.498	$C_4H_9NO_2$
71	3.74	0.252	C_3H_5NO
161	8.30	0.904	$C_7H_{15}NO_3$

5. Prediction of Structural Formulas of Boron Hydrides*

Lipscomb has developed a method for predicting the possible structural formulas for boron hydrides and ions of boron hydrides using equations of balance. The method is based on the consideration of the types of bonds that can be included in a boron hydrogen compound. These bonds are the boron-hydrogen-boron bridge bond, $\overset{H}{\underset{B\quad B}{\diagup\diagdown}}$, the boron-boron bond, B—B, the boron-hydrogen bonds, BH_2, and the three centered boron bonds, of which there are two types $\overset{B}{\underset{B}{\diagdown\diagup}}B$ and $\overset{B}{\underset{B\quad B}{\diagup\diagdown}}$. In a boron hydride compound or ion of the general formula $(B_pH_{p+q-c})^c$, where c is the charge (sign included), which is zero for neutral compounds, the possible number of bonds can be calculated using the following equations of balance.

$$t + y = p - q/2 - c$$
$$s = p + c - t$$
$$x = q + c - s$$

The s is the number of hydrogen bridge bonds, x is the number of BH_2 groups, t is the number of three centered boron bonds, and y is the number of boron-boron bonds. For a given boron hydrogen compound, the possible combinations of these terms that satisfy these equations can be deduced. Since there are only three equations and four unknowns, several combinations will be valid.

As an example, the method will be applied to the compound B_4H_{10}. For B_4H_{10}, p is 4, q is 6, and c is 0, so $t + y = 4 - 3 = 1$. The possible linear combinations of t and y satisfying this equation are $t = 0$, $y = 1$ and $y = 0$, $t = 1$. In the first case, the values of the other terms are $s = 4 + 0 - 0 = 4$ and

---

* Reference: W. N. Lipscomb, *Boron Hydrides*, W. A. Benjamin, Inc., New York, 1963.

$x = 6 + 0 - 4 = 2$. Consequently, the first possible structure for the hydride is no BBB bonds, one BB bond, four hydrogen bridge bonds, and two BH_2 units. The second possible structure is one BBB bond, no BB bonds, three hydrogen bridge bonds, and three BH_2 units. Generally the actual structure is the one with the highest degree of symmetry. Of the two possible structures, the first is the most symmetrical and can be represented as

Write a program to predict the possible structures in terms of the number of bonds of each type for boron hydrides and boron hydride ions. The p, q, and c values can be input. The main problem is to find the linear combinations of t and y satisfying the relationship $t + y = p - q/2 - c$. This can be done by determining the value of the right-hand term and then varying t and y independently from zero to this value. Each combination of t and y values that is found to satisfy the relationship can then be used to determine the s and x value. Each valid set of t, y, s, and x values corresponding to given p, q, and c values can then be output.

6. Crystallographic Analysis*

The reciprocal cell dimensions a', b', c', $\cos \alpha'$, $\cos \beta'$, and $\cos \gamma'$ are related to the actual cell dimensions by

$$\cos \beta' = \frac{\cos \gamma \cos \alpha - \cos \beta}{\sin \gamma \sin \alpha}$$

$$\cos \gamma' = \frac{\cos \alpha \cos \beta - \cos \gamma}{\sin \alpha \sin \beta}$$

$$\cos \alpha' = \frac{\cos \beta \cos \gamma - \cos \alpha}{\sin \beta \sin \gamma}$$

$$a' = \frac{1}{a \sin \beta \sin \gamma'}$$

---

* Reference: J. S. Rollett (Ed.), *Computing Methods in Crystallography*, Pergamon Press, New York, 1965.

$$b' = \frac{1}{b \sin \gamma \sin \alpha'}$$

$$c' = \frac{1}{c \sin \alpha \sin \beta'}.$$

Write a program to input the actual cell dimensions and output the reciprocal cell dimensions. The trigonometric identity, $\sin^2 x + \cos^2 x = 1$, will be useful in finding the sine values from the cosine values. Zeros should be used for cosines of 90°. Remember that radian measure arguments are used in FORTRAN trigonometric library functions.

The reciprocal unit cell dimensions and the Miller indices h, k, and l of a Bragg reflection can be used to calculate the parameter Q from which the interplanar distance d and the Bragg angle θ can be calculated. The Q parameter is found by the expression

$$Q = h^2a'^2 + k^2b'^2 + l^2c'^2 + 2klb'c' \cos \alpha' + 2lhc'a' \cos \beta' + 2hka'b' \cos \gamma'.$$

The interplanar distance d is equal to $Q^{-1/2}$ and has units of Angstroms if the original cell dimensions had units of Angstroms. The Bragg angle can be calculated by

$$\theta = \tan^{-1}\left[(\lambda^2 Q/(4 - \lambda^2 Q))^{1/2}\right]$$

where λ is the X-ray wavelength involved, measured in Angstrom units.

Write a program that will input the reciprocal unit cell dimensions, the Miller indices, and the X-ray wavelength; then calculate the Q value, the interplanar distance, and the Bragg angle. The results can then be output. This program could be combined with the previous program in order to do the calculations with the actual cell dimensions.

7. Spectrophotometric Analysis

Problem 1, Chapter 9, discusses the calculations involved in the spectrophotometric analysis of multicomponent solutions and Problem 5, Chapter 10, discusses the calculation of the ϵb (molar absorptivity times the cell thickness) from absorbance data for solutions of known concentration. Since multicomponent analysis involves the determination of the necessary ϵb values before the calculation of the concentrations of the components, it would be convenient to have a program that includes the combined calculations. Write a program that will accept absorbance data for solutions of each component, the concentrations of each of these solutions, and absorbance data for an unknown mixture of the components. Design the program to find the necessary ϵb values and calculate the unknown concentrations of the components of the mixture. Finally, output the results.

Bibliography for Part Two

General References

Pennington, R., *Introductory Computer Methods and Numerical Analysis*, The Macmillan Company, New York (1965)

Lee, J. A., *Numerical Analysis for Computers*, Reinhold Publishing Co., New York (1966)

Kuo, S. S., *Numerical Methods for Computers*, Addison-Wesley, Reading, Mass. (1965)

Hildebrand, F. B., *Introduction to Numerical Analysis*, McGraw-Hill Book Company, New York (1956)

Ledley, R. S., *Use of Computers in Biology and Medicine*, McGraw-Hill Book Company, New York (1965)

Wiberg, K., *Computer Programming for Chemists*, W. A. Benjamin, Inc., New York (1965)

Chapter 6

Freiser, H., and Q. Fernando, *Ionic Equilibria in Analytical Chemistry*, John Wiley and Sons, New York (1963)

Skoog, D. A., and D. M. West, *Fundamentals of Analytical Chemistry*, Holt, Rinehart and Winston, New York (1963)

Laitinen, H. A., *Chemical Analysis*, McGraw-Hill Book Company, New York (1960)

Chapter 7

Lance, G. N., Solutions of Algebraic and Transcendental Equations on an Automatic Digital Computer, *J. Assoc. Compt. Mach.*, **6**, 97 (1959)

Traub, J. F., *Iterative Methods for Solutions of Equations*, Prentice-Hall, Englewood Cliffs, N.J. (1964)

Chapter 8

Protter, M. H., and C. B. Morrey, *Calculus with Analytical Geometry*, Addison-Wesley, Reading, Mass. (1963)

Moore, W. S., *Physical Chemistry*, Prentice-Hall, Englewood Cliffs, N.J. (1962)

Rotenberg, A., A New Pseudo-Random Number Generator, *J. Assoc. Comput. Mach.*, 7, No. 1, 75 (1960)

Bauer, W. F., The Monte Carlo Method, *J. Soc. Ind. Appl. Math.*, No. 6, p. 438 (1958)

McCraken, D. D., The Monte Carlo Method, *Sci. Am.*, **192**, 90 (May 1955)

Chapter 9

Bellman, *Introduction to Matrix Algebra*, McGraw-Hill Book Company, New York (1960)

Fisier, R. C., and A. D. Zieberg, *Integrated Algebra and Trigonometry*, Prentice-Hall, Englewood Cliffs, N.J. (1967)

Fox, L., *Practical Solution of Linear Equations and Inversion of Matrices*, Appl. Math. Ser. U.S. Bur. Std., **39**, 1 (1954)

Beynon, J. H., *Mass Spectrometry and its Applications to Organic Chemistry*, Elsevier Publishing Co., New York (1960)

Baumann, W. R., *Absorption Spectroscopy*, John Wiley and Sons, New York (1962)

Skoog, D. A., and D. M. West, *Fundamentals of Analytical Chemistry*, Holt, Rinehart and Winston, New York (1963)

Chapter 10

Clenshaw, C. W., Curve Fitting with a Digital Computer, *Comput. J.*, p. 120 (1960)

Daniels, F., et al., *Experimental Physical Chemistry*, Prentice-Hall, Englewood Cliffs, N.J. (1963)

Mahan, Bruce H., *University Chemistry*, Addison-Wesley, Reading, Mass. (1965)

Moore, W. S., *Physical Chemistry*, Prentice-Hall, Englewood Cliffs, N.J. (1962)

Skoog, D. A., and D. M. West, *Fundamentals of Analytical Chemistry*, Holt, Rinehart and Winston, New York (1963)

Chapter 11

Goldstine, H. H., F. S. Murray, and J. Von Neuman, The Jacobi Method of Real Symmetric Matrices, *J. Assoc. Comput. Mach.*, **6**, 59 (1959)

Roberts, J. D., *Notes on Molecular Orbital Calculations*, W. A. Benjamin, Inc., New York (1962)

APPENDICES

Numerical Errors

Various types of errors can occur when calculations are carried out on a computer. The significance of the errors can be great if numerous repeated calculations are involved. The two most common types of error are round-off error and truncation error. Round-off errors arise as a result of the fixed number of digits that may constitute a number in storage, that is, an eight-digit mantissa. Repeated arithmetic manipulation of numbers can cause a loss of significant digits. This occurs because none of the intermediate results are rounded off. Thus, if the number of significant digits desired is close to the maximum number of digits that comprise a number in storage, erroneous results may be obtained. Frequently, calculations involve evaluations of functions, such as logarithms, in which the results are only finite approximations of a series. In fact, infinite series are used to evaluate many of the functions in the library subroutines. Since the maximum number of digits used for numbers is fixed, the series can be evaluated only to a certain number of digits and then truncated. If numerous approximations of this type are made, accumulation of errors can occur.

Many of the numerical methods employed for calculation purposes are approximation methods and thus give only approximations as results. For example, the determination of roots by iteration or the evaluation of a definite integral by Simpson's Rule are approximation methods, and the results obtained should be considered only approximations. Occasionally the loss of significant figures can be avoided by proper designing of the calculation steps. For example, a subtraction of two numbers that are very nearly equal can result in loss of significant digits, and the calculations should be altered, if possible, to avoid this subtraction.

FORTRAN Errors

Most FORTRAN compilers have error routines that are designed to detect errors in the use of the FORTRAN language. When an error is detected, an error message is output by the compiler. These error messages are usually in the form of error codes, and the codes used differ somewhat for various types of compilers. The error codes given below are for the FORTRAN II D compiler used in the IBM 1620 computers. Since the error codes differ for various computer systems, this list is intended as an example of a typical error code list. Error code lists for other types of compilers are normally available from the director of the computer installation or from the manufacturer of the computer for which the compiler is designed.

Phase I errors: When errors of this type are detected during compilation, an error message like the following is output:

LLLL + PPPP ERROR *n*

where LLLL is the statement number of the last numbered statement that had been processed prior to the detection of the error, PPPP indicates the number of statements following statement LLLL that have been processed before the detection of the error, and *n* is a code number indicating the type of error. The statement containing the error is located PPPP statements past statement LLLL. The error codes and their meanings are listed below.

Error No.	*Condition*
1	Undeterminable, misspelled, or incorrectly formed statement.
2	Syntax error in a nonarithmetic statement (exception: DO statements).
3	Dimensioned variable used improperly, that is, without subscripting, or subscripting appears on a variable not previously dimensioned.
4	Symbol table full (processing may not be continued).
5	Incorrect subscript.
6	Same statement number assigned to more than one statement.
7	Control transferred to FORMAT statement.
8	Variable name greater than six alphameric characters.
9	Variable name used both as a nondimensioned variable name and as a Subroutine or Function name.
10	Invalid variable within an EQUIVALENCE statement.
11	Subroutine or Function name or dummy variable used in an EQUIVALENCE statement (subprogram only).
12	k not equal to $f + 2$ for equivalence of fixed-point to floating-point variables.
13	Within an Equivalence list, placement of two variables previously in Common, or one variable previously equivalenced and another either equivalenced or placed in Common.
14	Sense Switch number missing in an IF (Sense Switch *n*) statement.
15	Statement number or numbers missing, not separated by commas, or nonnumerical in a transfer statement.
16	Index of a computed GO TO missing, invalid, or not preceded by a comma.
17	Fixed-point number greater than k digits.
18	Invalid floating-point number.
19	Incorrect subscripting within a DIMENSION statement.
20	First character of a name not alphabetic.

Error No.	*Condition*
21	Variable within a DIMENSION statement previously used as a non-dimensioned variable, or previously dimensioned or used as a Subroutine or Function name.
22	Dimensioned variable used within an arithmetic statement function.
23	More than four continuation cards.
24	Statement number in a DO statement appeared on a previous statement.
25	Syntax error in a DO statement.
26	FORMAT number missing in an input/output statement.
27	Statement number in an input/output statement appeared previously on a statement other than a FORMAT statement, or a number on a FORMAT statement appeared in other than an input/output statement.
28	Syntax error in input/output list or an invalid list element.
29	Syntax error in CALL statement, or an invalid argument.
30	SUBROUTINE or FUNCTION statement not the first statement in a subprogram.
31	Syntax error or invalid parameter in a SUBROUTINE or FUNCTION statement.
32	Syntax error or invalid variable in a COMMON statement.
33	Variable in a Common list previously placed in Common or previously equivalenced.
34	Library function name appeared to the left of an equal sign or in a COMMON, EQUIVALENCE, DIMENSION, or input/output statement; or function name not followed by a left parenthesis.
35	Syntax error in FORMAT statement, or invalid FORMAT specifications.
36	Invalid expression to the left of an equal sign in an arithmetic expression.
37	Arithmetic statement function not preceding the first executable statement.
38	Invalid expression in an IF or CALL statement, or invalid expression to the right of an equal sign in an arithmetic statement.
39	Unbalanced parentheses.
40	Invalid argument used in calling an arithmetic statement function or Function subprogram.
41	DO loop ended with a transfer statement.
42	No statement number for next executable statement following a transfer statement.
43	Improperly ended nonarithmetic statement.
44	Unnumbered CONTINUE statement.
45	Number of Common addresses assigned in excess of storage capacity because of Equivalence.
46	Statement number or subscript greater than 9999 (only first four significant digits are retained).
47	RETURN statement appeared in program other than a subprogram (statement ignored).
48	RETURN statement not contained in a Subroutine or Function subprogram.
49	Statement number not defined.

Phase II errors: These errors are detected during a postcompilation period, and the error messages output may be one or more of the following:

    XXXX SYMBOL TABLE FULL
    XXXX DO TABLE FULL
    XXXX IMPROPER DO NESTING
    XXXX MIXED MODE

The XXXX is the relative number of the statement in which the error is detected. The most common of these errors are the last two. The first two are seldom encountered in small programs.

The library subroutines have error-detection routines in them; thus errors can be detected when a given subroutine is used. The errors are detected during execution of the program and not during compilation. Generally the detection of an error of this type results in the output of an error code. The result of the library subroutine computation is then set at the most reasonable value and the program continues. For example, if a negative number is used as the argument of the SQRTF subroutine, an error message is output and then the square root of the absolute value of the number is found and computation continues. The library-subroutine error codes and their meanings are given below.

    E1 Overflow in FAD or FSB
    E2 Underflow in FAD or FSB
    E3 Overflow in FMP
    E4 Underflow in FMP
    E5 Overflow in FDV or FDVR
    E6 Underflow in FDV or FDVR
    E7 Zero division in FDV or FDVR
    E8 Zero division in FXD or FXDR
    E9 Overflow in FIX
    F1 Loss of all significance in FSIN or FCOS
    F2 Zero argument in FLN
    F3 Negative argument in FLN
    F4 Overflow in FEXP
    F5 Underflow in FEXP
    F6 Negative argument in FAXB
        Negative argument in FSQR
    F7 Input data in incorrect form or outside the allowable range
    F8 Output data outside the allowable range
    F9 Input or output record longer than 80 or 87 characters (whichever is applicable to the I/0 medium being used)
    G1 Zero to minus power in FIXI
    G2 Fixed-point number to negative power in FIXI
    G3 Overflow in FIXI
    G4 Floating-point zero to negative power in FAXI
    G5 Overflow in FAXI
    G6 Underflow in FAXI
    G7 Zero to negative power in FAXB

APPENDIX 2

Monitor and Batch Processing

Compilation of source programs is greatly facilitated by operating the computer so that the control of processing is accomplished by a program in storage called a monitor. When auxiliary storage is available in the form of a magnetic disk, the monitor program can be conveniently called into storage for use. Furthermore, the disk storage provides enough extra storage space so that the complete compilation and execution of programs can be handled as a single processing job. One of the most useful aspects of processing under monitor control is that batch processing of source programs can be done conveniently. That is, source programs can be stacked and then input, compiled, and executed in sequence. This method provides for the most efficient use of the computer. The monitor is actually a machine language program which contains a supervisory program that controls the processing. A FORTRAN compiler is also included in the monitor and is used for compilation of source programs as directed by the supervisor program.

The monitor is controlled, that is, directed to do specific processing jobs, by monitor control records or messages. These control records must be introduced by the programmer or computer operator and must precede the source program. In fact, in batch processing, each source program must be preceded by the job describing monitor control records. Examples of these monitor control records for use with the IBM 1620 FORTRAN II D compiler appear below. For a similar discussion of monitor control methods, the monitor specifications manual for the system used should be consulted.

‡‡JOBbn $n = 5$ for card input $n = 1$ for typewriter input   ‡ is a special character called a record mark (0-2-8 card punch code). This control record initiates the job and indicates the mode of input to be used.

‡‡FORbn $n = 5$ for card input $n = 1$ for typewriter input   b = blank space.

This control record indicates that the processing job is to

be a FORTRAN compilation only and gives the mode of input of the source program.

‡‡FORX*n*   *n* = 5 for card input   *n* = 1 for typewriter input.

This control record indicates that the processing job is to be a FORTRAN compilation, followed by the execution of the compiled program. This is a very useful control record because it allows for execution to follow the compilation of a source program immediately. Of course, if any data are to be used by the program during execution, they must be available in order to be read in by the program.

‡‡XEQSbbbbbbbbbbbbbbbbbbbbbb*n*   *n* = 5 for card input   *n* = 1 for typewriter input   b = blank space. Some of the other positions are used in certain cases.

This control record is used to load and execute the object program form of a FORTRAN program.

‡‡DUPb*n*   *n* = 5 for card input   *n* = 1 for typewriter input   b = blank space.

This control record calls for the use of the disk utility program, which is part of the monitor. The disk utility program manipulates information between disk storage and computer storage.

‡‡‡‡   This is a control record that indicates the end of the processing job. This record is placed after each batch of source statements and data (if any).

In addition to monitor control records, several FORTRAN compiler control records can direct the compiler to accomplish certain tasks. These control records should precede any source program statements but must follow any monitor control records. The most useful of these control records are given below.

∗POBJP*n*   *n* = 4 for punched card output. The first character must be an asterisk. This control record results in an object program being output (punched) after compilation. The object program can be loaded and executed using an ‡‡XEQS monitor control record. An object deck is very useful if a program is to be used many times, for it does not require compilation.

∗FANDK*ffkk*   This control record permits the variation of the allowable length of integers and real numbers used in the computer. The *ff* consists of two digits indicating the desired length of the mantissa of real numbers and the *kk* consists of two digits indicating the desired length of integers. The allowable range of *ff* is 02 to 28; the range for *kk* is 04 to 10. This control record can be used to decrease the amount of storage used by real numbers and integers in cases where a great deal of storage is being used and space must be conserved. It can also be used to increase the length of integers and real numbers so that more significant digits can be used in calculations. However, the characteristics of real numbers are always limited to two digits. When expanded length numbers are used, the time required for calculation can be greatly increased. If a subprogram uses a control record of this type, the main program utilizing the subprogram must have a similar control record.

*LDISKNNNNNN This control record causes the object program to be permanently stored in the magnetic disk storage area. The NNNNNN is a one-to-six character name that can be given to the program for reference purposes. In the case of subprograms, this will be the name of the subprogram. If the program stored on the disk is a main program, it can be read into computer storage from the disk and executed by an ‡‡XEQS control record like ‡‡XEQSNNNNNN.

The *DLOADNNNNNN control record in which NNNNNN is the program name can be used with ‡‡DUP monitor control record to provide for the recording of an object program on the disk. The program can then be referred to by the name. The *DELETNNNNNN control record in which NNNNNN is the program name can be used with the ‡‡DUP monitor control record to remove the named program from the disk. This is used whenever it is no longer desirable to have a program or subprogram on the disk.

The normal arrangement of the control records and a program for processing purposes is

‡‡JOB 5
‡‡FORX5 (or ‡‡FOR 5 or ‡‡XEQS · · ·) (or ‡‡DUP 5)
Any FORTRAN control records desired
FORTRAN source program (or object program for ‡‡XEQS and ‡‡DUP 5)
Data to be used by source program (if any)
‡‡‡‡End of job record

Each program to be subjected to a processing job should be preceded by the proper control records. To save processing time, each program, where convenient, should have a CALL EXIT statement. This statement, which is usually the last executable statement in a program, will result in a branch back to the monitor so that the monitor can immediately continue with the next processing job.

APPENDIX 3

Subprogram Linkage with Main Programs

Linkage of a subprogram with a main program can usually be accomplished when the computer system is under monitor control. The linkage procedure depends on the design of the computer system being used. Hence the appropriate monitor specifications manual should be consulted for the proper linkage method. If the programmer is operating the computer, information concerning the linkage procedure can generally be obtained from the director of the computer installation. If the program is submitted for processing, a precise description indicating that a subprogram is to be used with the main program should be submitted with the processing request. To illustrate the linkage procedure, the technique used with the IBM 1620 FORTRAN II D compiler under monitor control is discussed below.

Subprograms are self-contained routines designed for use with main programs. The subprograms must be compiled before use with a main program. The normal procedure followed is to prepare the source subprogram along with the main source program. Then the subprogram and the main program can be compiled and the main program executed in a batch-processing operation. In such cases, the compiled subprogram is usually stored on the disk and then called in from the disk for use by the main program. The sequence of control records and programs to accomplish this is

‡‡JOB 5
‡‡FOR 5   Just compilation and no execution
∗LDISKNNNNNN   NNNNNN is the name of the subprogram
Subprogram source program
‡‡‡‡
‡‡JOB 5
‡‡FORX5
Any FORTRAN control records desired
Main source program. (The subprogram is used by the main program by
    referring to it by name.)

Data to be used by source program (if any)

‡‡‡‡

‡‡JOB 5

‡‡DUP 5 This job provides for the deletion of the subprogram from the disk.

*DELETNNNNNN   It should be deleted if it is not to be used again in the near future.

Often a subprogram is a general routine that can be used with many other programs. If a general subprogram is to be used, it can be stored on the disk semipermanently and called into use by any main program. The calling of the subprogram is accomplished by using the name of the subprogram in an arithmetic statement if the subprogram is a FUNCTION subprogram or by using a CALL statement if the subprogram is a SUBROUTINE subprogram. An object program for a subprogram can be obtained by the following sequence of control records:

‡‡JOB 5

‡‡FOR5

*POBJP4

Subprogram source program

‡‡‡‡

Once the object program is available, it can be used with a main program by reading in the subprogram when the main program is being executed. Actually, when a subprogram is called by a main program, the monitor will check to see if the subprogram is on the disk; if it is not, the following message will be output:

LOAD NNNNNN   where NNNNNN is the subprogram name

After this message is typed, the object program of the subprogram is then read in. A control record such as *DATA must follow the object program to indicate to the monitor that the last card of the subprogram has been read in and execution can continue. Of course, the subprogram object program must precede any data to be utilized by the main program. Otherwise some data may be mistakenly read in as a subprogram. The *DATA control record essentially separates the subprogram from any data, but this control record must be present even if no data are used by the main program.

The sequence of control records and programs used for the loading of the object subprogram from the card reader is

‡‡JOB 5

‡‡FORX5 (or ‡‡XEQS ···)

Any FORTRAN control records desired

Main source program (or main object program)

Subprogram object program

*DATA
Data to be used by the main program (if any)
‡‡‡‡

If desirable, the subprogram object program can be recorded on the disk just prior to compilation and execution of the main program. The following sequence of control records can be used.

‡‡JOB 5
‡‡DUP 5
*DLOADNNNNNN   NNNNNN is the name of the subprogram
Subprogram object program
‡‡‡‡
‡‡JOB 5
‡‡FORX5 (or ‡‡XEQS ···)
Any FORTRAN control records desired
Main source program (or main object program)
Data to be used by main program (if any)
‡‡‡‡
‡‡JOB 5
‡‡DUP 5
*DELETNNNNNN   NNNNNN is the name of the subprogram
‡‡‡‡

Comparison of FORTRAN II and FORTRAN IV

FORTRAN IV, a more sophisticated version of the FORTRAN language, possesses several features that FORTRAN II lacks. Ideally, FORTRAN II is a subset of FORTRAN IV, which means that a FORTRAN II program could be used with a FORTRAN IV compiler. This is possible with only slight modifications of the FORTRAN II program. Most FORTRAN II programs can be converted to FORTRAN IV programs by changing only a few statements. The most important of these changes are in the input and the output statements, as discussed below. The following list points out the differences and similarities between the two versions of FORTRAN.

	FORTRAN II	FORTRAN IV
Arithmetic statements	Real and integer constants and variables. No mixed mode except real with integer exponents.	Real and integer constants and variables. Mixed mode is permitted with some compilers. Wide variety of other constant and variable types.
Input statements	ACCEPT n, list READ n, list WRITE OUTPUT TAPE m, n, list. (For magnetic tape-oriented computers only.)	READ (m, n) list m = integer code giving the input device. n = FORMAT statement number.
Output statements	TYPE n, list PUNCH n, list PRINT n, list WRITE OUTPUT TAPE m, n, list. (For magnetic tape-oriented computers only.)	WRITE (m, n) list m = integer code giving the input device. n = FORMAT statement number.

	FORTRAN II	FORTRAN IV
Control statements	GO TO n	Same as II
	GO TO $(n_1, n_2, \ldots, n_m)$, i.	Same as II
	Available on 709/7090 IBM Computers	GO TO i, $(n_1, n_2, \ldots, n_m)$. The program branches to statement number in parentheses, which is same as current value of i. The value of i is set by an ASSIGN statement, such as ASSIGN 5 TO I
	IF (X) n_1, n_2, n_3.	Same as II
	Not available	IF (A) s (s is a complete statement). If A is true statement, s is executed. If A is false, the program skips s and goes to next instruction. A represents a logical expression involving variables and constants with the logical operations .AND., .OR., and .NOT., and/or the relational operations .LT. ($<$), .LE. ($\leq$), .EQ. ($=$), .NE. ($\neq$), .GT. ($>$) and .GE. ($\geq$).
	Not available	IF (A) n_1, n_2. If A is true, the program branches to statement n_1. Otherwise the program branches to n_2. A is a logical expression.
	PAUSE	Same as II
	STOP	Same as II
	CONTINUE	Same as II
	END	Same as II
	CALL EXIT	Same as II
	Precedes END statement and gives control back to the monitor. Used only for systems using monitor.	
	EQUIVALENCE	Generally same as II
	COMMON	Generally same as II
Arithmetic statement function	$A(v_1, \cdots, v_n) = f(v_1, \cdots, v_n)$	Same as II except the name, A does not have to end in F as is the case with some FORTRAN II compilers.
Library subroutines	X = LIBF(Y)	The library subroutine names do not generally end in F. Some of the names differ from the names used in II and more library subroutines are available.

	FORTRAN II	FORTRAN IV
Function subprogram	FUNCTION name (list)	Generally the same as II except the name does not have to end in F as is the case with some FORTRAN II compilers. Furthermore, the type of variable used in the subprogram can be specified, such as REAL FUNCTION name (list).
Subroutine subprograms	SUBROUTINE name (list) CALL name (list) RETURN	Generally same as II Same as II Same as II
Subscripted variables	Up to three subscripts allowed. DIMENSION $v(n_1, \ldots, n_m)$	Same as II except some compilers allow for more subscripts. Generally same as II
Format statements	n FORMAT (specification list) I, E, F, H, X, and A specifications.	n FORMAT (specification list) I, E, F, H, X, and A specifications. Additional specifications, such as D and L. Provides for inclusion of literal data without H specification and allows for variable formats.

The Dw.d, the double precision specification, allows for the storage and output of numbers with twice as many digits as E or F mode numbers. Double precision numbers can be set up in the same way that E mode numbers are set up except that the E is replaced by a D.

The Lw is the logical information specification and allows for the input or output of logical information. Logical information is stored and output as either true, T, or false, F.

Literal data can be accommodated in FORMAT statements without H specification. This is done by including the literal constants within apostrophes. For example, n FORMAT ('LITERAL MESSAGE') contains the literal data LITERAL MESSAGE for output purposes or reserves 15 spaces for input purposes. This is available on only a few compilers.

FORTRAN IV also provides for variable formating. That is, it provides for the input of FORMAT statements as data. This is accomplished by permitting a variable name rather than a statement number in a READ statement. Thus the FORMAT may be read in using A specification and given a variable name. This variable name can then be used to refer to the FORMAT. For example, the sequence of statements needed to provide for a variable format is shown in the following example.

READ (5, 1) FRMAT
1 FORMAT (12A6)   This specification provides for the input of 12 groups
–   of six characters or a card containing the desired
–   FORMAT.

READ (5, FRMAT) X, I   In this read statement, the variable name FRMAT is
            used to refer to the previously input FORMAT state-
            ment that specifies the form of X and Y.

The available FORTRAN IV compilers have many other types of statements and format specifications. An appropriate manual can be consulted for these additional statements.

Some of the FORTRAN statements and variable types are not common to all computer systems. The differences between FORTRAN II and FORTRAN IV have been emphasized in the text. It is important to learn the limitations of the computer system that you will be using. Several computer models are listed below, along with the type of compiler most commonly used with each computer. Each computer is given a code number for reference purposes.

Code Number	Computer Model	FORTRAN Compiler Type
1	CDC 3100	II
2	CDC 3400	IV
3	CDC 6600	IV
4	GE 200 series	II
5	GE 600 series	IV
6	IBM 360	IV
7	IBM 1401	IV
8	IBM 1620	II-D (disk oriented)
9	IBM 7090	II and IV
10	RCA Spectra 70	IV
11	SDS 920	II
12	SDS 920	IV
13	UNIVAC III	IV

Listed below are some statements and variable types that are not common to all computers in the preceding list. The computers for which these statements and variables can be used are indicated by code number. All other statements and variable types discussed in this book can be used with any of the computers in the preceding list. Of course, statements and variable types that are exclusively for FORTRAN IV can only be used with computers having FORTRAN IV compilers as indicated in the above list. For a description of the capabilities of a given FORTRAN compiler, the appropriate language specification manual should be consulted.

Statement of Variable Type	Computer Code Number
ACCEPT	8, 11
READ	1, 2, 3, 4, 5, 6, 8, 9, 10, 11, 13
PRINT	1, 2, 3, 4, 5, 6, 8, 9, 10, 11, 13
PUNCH	1, 2, 3, 4, 5, 6, 8, 9, 10, 11, 13
TYPE	8, 11

READ (n, m), WRITE (n, m)	1, 2, 3, 5, 6, 7, 9(IV), 10, 12, 13
WRITE OUTPUT TAPE, READ OUTPUT TAPE	1, 2, 3, 4, 9(II), 11
ASSIGN GO TO	1, 2, 3, 4, 5, 6, 9, 10, 11, 12, 13
CALL EXIT	5, 6, 8, 9, 10, 13
ARITHMETIC STATEMENT FUNCTION	1, 2, 3, 4, 5, 6, 8, 9, 10, 11, 13
DOUBLE PRECISION variable and constant	2, 3, 5, 6, 9(IV), 10, 12
COMPLEX variable and constant	2, 3, 5, 6, 9(IV), 10, 12
LOGICAL variable and constant	5, 6, 7, 9(IV), 10, 12, 13

INDEX